# UPSTAGERS

# THE FLOOD

## Charles Way

### Extension Material
### Stephen Cockett and Michael Wardley

## CollinsEducational
*An imprint of* HarperCollins*Publishers*

## Acknowledgements

*The Flood* was first performed at the Unicorn Theatre for Children on 3 March 1990.

The authors and publisher would like to thank the following for permission to reproduce illustrations and photographs:
Shirley Trevena, front cover illustration; Sheila Burnett, back cover photograph; Nigel Luckhurst, page 53; DHA Lighting Limited, pages 57, 58, 60; Dave Sumner, pages 62, 65, 76; Mike Dodd, page 66; Network Photographers, page 79; Mary Evans Picture Library, page 88.

The authors and publisher would like to thank the following for permission to reproduce copyright material:
HarperCollins*Publishers* for the *Good News Bible* extracts on page 78; East Lindsey District Council for the extracts from *Guidance Notes on Coastal Flooding* on page 80; Chatto and Windus for the extract from 'Noj and the Flood' from *Beginnings* by Penelope Farmer; California Press for 'Mount Rainier and the Great Flood' from *Indian Legends of the Pacific Northwest*; Faber and Faber Ltd for the extract from *The Mysteries* by Tony Harrison.

Although every effort has been made to contact the copyright-holders, this has not proved to be possible in every case. We apologise for any inadvertent infringements of copyright.

Published by CollinsEducational
*An imprint of* HarperCollins*Publishers*
77–85 Fulham Palace Road
Hammersmith
London W6 8JB

ISBN 0 00 330304 7

First published in 1992

Designed by Dave Sumner
Typeset in Century Schoolbook by
Northern Phototypesetting Co Ltd, Bolton

Printed and bound in Great Britain by
Scotprint Ltd, Musselburgh

# CONTENTS

## Act One

## Act Two

# CAST

**Martha**
**Gerald**
**Tony**  (age six)
**Rebecca**  (age twelve)

## *Note*

The play begins in the mind of Martha, with a dream in which symbols are all important. Martha wakes up a few moments later, but in a design sense we should remain in a symbolic world. All that is needed, in order to tell the story, is what is mentioned. Attempts to create a real house should be avoided.

# ACT ONE

## SCENE 1 • THE DREAM

**CHORUS**  Once upon a time,
the clouds gathered in the heavens,
all clouds becoming one cloud;
a cloud without end or beginning,
and the first raindrops fell
pitter pat, pitter pat,
on unsuspecting heads.
Pitter pat, pitter pat
they slipped down the windows and walls
of the world,
and the world went on its busy ways
of work and pleasure;
feeding from the fat of the land,
felling the trees of the forest,
slaying the beasts of the plain,
until the rain rose from the gutters
and the waters became one water
wetting the feet of the fearless world.
Pitter pat, pitter pat it fell
on unsuspecting heads.
Pitter pat, pitter pat it fell,
disturbing only the dreams of a few.
Pitter pat,
pitter pat,
pitter pat.
Disturbing only the dreams
only the dreams
only the dreams
of a few.

*Lights fade to darkness, and slowly rise to reveal on the backcloth a
silhouette of a city landscape. As this happens we hear rain as it develops
from drips into a downpour.*
   *The lights rise further to reveal centre stage a small dinghy, floating, as
it were. In the dinghy is* **Martha**. *She is collapsed unconscious over the*

1

*side and she is in her dressing gown. The rain fades, and we hear the sound of wind becoming louder and louder. This brings her to consciousness (within the dream). The wind blows over her, and the cityscape disappears. Inside the dinghy are several symbolic items which begin, magically, to lift, as if by themselves, from the dinghy into mid air. These are a briefcase, a toy clown and a pair of dancing shoes.* **Martha** *tries to reach them, but as happens in dreams, she has no strength. The wind dies down very suddenly and on the backcloth emerges the shape of a single tree. The light becomes very bright, and the sun burns. Suddenly a large black bird, made of paper (like a kite), flies above her, and makes as if to attack her. As she cowers a white bird, similarly made, enters, and the black bird falls. She gets out of the dinghy and it is pulled away. She takes from the beak of the white bird a twig. The white bird flies away. Strange music is heard, as at the end of the play. Lights fade as she stands alone centre stage.*

*The city silhouette returns.*

# SCENE 2 • MARTHA'S WARNING

**Gerald** *enters dressed in a suit, or getting dressed as the scene progresses.*

**GERALD**          (*softly*) Martha. Martha. (*loudly*) Martha.

*The children,* **Tony** *and* **Rebecca,** *enter still in night gear.* **Tony** *clutches a toy clown.*

Martha!

**Martha** *is unmoved and stares in front of her.*

| | |
|---|---|
| **TONY** | What's going on? |
| **GERALD** | Shut up, Tony. Martha, wake up. Martha – Damn it! |
| **REBECCA** | Brown Owl says you shouldn't wake sleepwalkers. |
| **TONY** | Is mum asleep? |
| **REBECCA** | Sleepwalking – to be precise. |
| **TONY** | She looks funny. |
| **GERALD** | Go and get dressed. |
| **TONY** | I want to see. |
| **GERALD** | *Out!* |
| **REBECCA** | Please. (*She pushes* **Tony** *out.*) |
| **GERALD** | Martha. I'm going to be late. Martha, if you can hear me, blink your eyes. (*Nothing happens.*) Martha, it's – I'm late. (*screaming*) Martha! |

*The children run back in, frightened.*

*Out!*

*They run out again.*

All right, Martha, you can stay like that all day, I do not care.

*He turns to go.*                                                                    3

| | |
|---|---|
| **MARTHA** | Is it still raining? |
| **GERALD** | You're awake? |
| **MARTHA** | Gerald? |
| **GERALD** | I'm going to be late. |
| **MARTHA** | I had the dream again – and yet I can't remember . . . |
| **GERALD** | The most important day of my career and you oversleep. |
| **MARTHA** | I'm sorry – I – |
| **GERALD** | Rebecca. Tony. Breakfast. |
| **MARTHA** | Is it still raining? |
| **GERALD** | Look shipshape. |
| **MARTHA** | (*closing her eyes*) Shipshape? |
| **GERALD** | Martha, stay awake, stay awake. |
| **MARTHA** | I am awake, aren't I? |
| **GERALD** | You're losing your grip on reality. |
| **MARTHA** | No, I – |
| **GERALD** | A person who does not know if they are asleep or awake, dreaming or not dreaming, is a person who is losing their grip on reality. Breakfast! |
| **MARTHA** | I must talk to you. |
| **GERALD** | Are you going to get their breakfast, or am I? |
| **MARTHA** | I must talk. |
| **GERALD** | All right, I'll get their breakfast, I'll get them off to school, I'll do it – you skunk around in your slippers like you did yesterday and the day before that. |
| **MARTHA** | Gerald. |
| **GERALD** | Not now. The kids'll be late for school. I'll be late for school. |
| **MARTHA** | You'll be late for school? |
| **GERALD** | Work, I meant work. I'll be late. |
| **MARTHA** | Does it matter? |
| **GERALD** | Does it matter? The most important day of my career. Today I take over, I sign the deals, I make the money. Nothing will ever be the same again – believe me. We're going to be rich – very, very rich. Does that matter? Yes, it matters. |

*Enter* **Rebecca** *with newspaper.*

4

| | |
|---|---|
| GERALD | Shreddies? Puffs? Splitz? Pops? Flakes? Nuts? Crispies or Bran? What, what? Tony. |

Rebecca *is reading the paper.*

| | |
|---|---|
| | Rebecca. |
| REBECCA | I'm here, I'm here. |
| GERALD | And I mean rich. |
| REBECCA | Pops, no Crispies, no Puffs, no Flakes. |
| GERALD | God save me – Take it, take it. |
| REBECCA | Look there's been more floods. |

Martha *reaches for the paper but* Gerald *snatches it.*

| | |
|---|---|
| REBECCA | And it's still raining. All last night it rained. I couldn't sleep. |
| MARTHA | Gerald – about the rain. |
| REBECCA | The netball will be cancelled again. |
| MARTHA | I had the same dream – it's so strange. |
| GERALD | Yes, yes, we know the dream, the wind, the black bird and the white bird. We know the dream. We're not interested in your subconscious anxieties. |
| MARTHA | This time was different. It was more than a dream. I felt as if . . . |
| GERALD | Your dream doesn't matter. It's not real and it frightens the children. |
| REBECCA | No it doesn't. |

*Enter* Tony, *dressed, with a very serious face, walking slowly and holding a goldfish bowl. There is a dead fish in the bowl. He puts it on the breakfast table with an ominous thud.*

| | |
|---|---|
| TONY | Arthur's dead. |
| MARTHA | He was getting old – for a fish. |
| TONY | He was alive last night. |
| REBECCA | Maybe he drowned. |
| MARTHA | Rebecca. |
| REBECCA | Maybe you overfed him and he choked on his own sick. |
| GERALD | Ha! |

5

| | |
|---|---|
| MARTHA | That's not funny. |
| TONY | You fed him last night. He was alive before you fed him. |
| REBECCA | So! It's just a goldfish. It's not a relative or anything. |
| TONY | What shall I do with him? |
| MARTHA | We'll do the right thing. |
| REBECCA | Feed it to next door's cat. |
| TONY | Mum. |
| REBECCA | Brown Owl says we should recycle all our waste. |
| TONY | He's not waste. He's my fish. |
| REBECCA | Was. |

*Rebecca makes a fish face at Tony and he loses control. He chases her, shouting as he does so.*

| | |
|---|---|
| GERALD | Ha! |
| MARTHA | Children. Tony, stop that! Rebecca. |
| GERALD | Perhaps you should see someone. |
| MARTHA | What? |

*The children fall suddenly silent.*

| | |
|---|---|
| GERALD | I said (*pause*) . . . perhaps you should see someone. |
| MARTHA | Who? |
| GERALD | I don't know – a psychiatrist. |
| TONY | What's that? |
| MARTHA | I don't need a psychiatrist. I need you. |
| TONY | What's going on? |
| MARTHA | I need to talk – now. |
| GERALD | Not in front of them. |
| TONY | Why? |
| GERALD | Your mother isn't very well. |
| TONY | Is that true? Is it? |
| MARTHA | I . . . (*shrugging*) I have this dream . . . |
| GERALD | Martha! I'll get you another goldfish. |
| REBECCA | Boring. |
| MARTHA | Don't be cruel. |
| REBECCA | Why not? (*pause*) |

6

| | |
|---|---|
| TONY | Has my fish gone to Heaven? |
| REBECCA | Heaven doesn't exist, does it, Dad? There's only the here and now. The rest is all make-believe like Father Christmas. |
| TONY | Is that true? |
| MARTHA | There are things that your father and sister and even Brown Owl do not understand. There are other worlds besides this one. Your fish is at peace. Peace is another world, another place where people are not cruel. |
| TONY | Is Arthur there? |
| MARTHA | I hope so. |
| GERALD | The fish is dead – that's all. I'll get you one that works. I must go. |
| MARTHA | Gerald . . . Gerald you can't go – not today. |
| GERALD | Rebecca. |

*As is their routine,* **Rebecca** *brings him his coat and hat.*

| | |
|---|---|
| MARTHA | Please, (*dropping to her knees*) I . . . I beg you. |

*Silence. They all stare at* **Martha**.

| | |
|---|---|
| TONY | Mum? |

**Rebecca** *then brings a briefcase to her father but* **Martha** *grabs it.*

| | |
|---|---|
| GERALD | Martha. |
| MARTHA | In the dream I had last night, something new happened. |
| GERALD | Give me the briefcase. |
| MARTHA | No. |
| GERALD | Are you crazy? |
| MARTHA | If you won't talk to me, then just listen. |
| GERALD | Give me my briefcase. Give it me. (*They struggle for it.*) Give it. |
| REBECCA | Stop fighting! You're always fighting. |

**Martha** *pulls away with the case.*

| | |
|---|---|
| GERALD | The most important day . . . |

| | |
|---|---|
| **MARTHA** | Something new happened. My dream took place at sea. |

*Silence.*

| | |
|---|---|
| **GERALD** | All right, you have the case. You talk. Then I'll have the case and I'll go to work. |
| **MARTHA** | How long has it been raining? |
| **TONY** | Three days. |
| **MARTHA** | And three nights of solid rain. |
| **GERALD** | You want to talk about the weather? |
| **MARTHA** | It's not going to stop raining. The dream, you see. It's not going to stop raining until everything is destroyed, swept away. (*She grabs the newspaper.*) Look, look! It's started, accidents caused by floods, and, and it isn't going to stop until the whole world is beneath water, the buildings, the animals, the people. You have to stay here and think of a way of escaping, surviving the flood. |

*Silence.*

| | |
|---|---|
| **TONY** | Is that true? |
| **GERALD** | No, Tony, that isn't true. Martha you're not well. I didn't realise how . . . but we'll sort it out. |
| **REBECCA** | Dad? |
| **GERALD** | Don't worry. Your mother is just teasing. A game. The world is not going to end. I mean, what would be the point of me going to work if the world was going to end – which it isn't – it's never ending. |

*He takes* **Martha** *to one side.*

| | |
|---|---|
| | We'll talk later, tonight, in depth, for as long as you want. I promise, I promise. |

**Rebecca** *gives him his umbrella.*

| | |
|---|---|
| **GERALD** | I don't think I'll be needing that. |
| **TONY** | Don't forget my goldfish. |

*Exit* **Gerald**. *A moment later he returns and picks up the umbrella, smiles and leaves.*

8

# SCENE 3 • MARTHA AND THE CHILDREN

**Martha** *turns and the children back away from her. She switches on a transistor radio.*

RADIO         The heavy rains of the past few days continue this morning. The weather forecasters are uncertain as to the exact cause of the freak downpour, which is causing chaos in low-lying parts of the country. Farmers have been badly hit as rivers burst their banks, drowning large numbers of animals. Our western transmitter is temporarily out of order because of the rain, and there are severe flood warnings on the rivers. (*Then there follows a list of rivers . . . Thames, Severn, Wye, etc.*)

*The reception fades, returns and fades for good.* **Martha** *shakes the radio, then turns it off.*

MARTHA        It's true, and it's not going to stop. You don't believe me? Look. Look at the paper! Read it, Rebecca. Read it!
REBECCA       No.
MARTHA        Read it!
REBECCA       No – you can't make me.
TONY          Are we going to school?

**Martha** *takes the children by the arm.*

REBECCA       Let go of me.
MARTHA        Look. Look out at the window.

*They gaze out at the audience.*

              Have you ever seen rain like that before?

| | |
|---|---|
| TONY | No. |
| REBECCA | Yes. |
| TONY | Not like that. |
| REBECCA | It's rain, ordinary rain. The type we get on holiday in Cornwall. |
| MARTHA | You're not looking, you're not seeing. It's different. |
| TONY | No wind, just straight lines of rain. |
| REBECCA | She's trying to frighten us. |
| TONY | Are you? |
| MARTHA | Yes. It is frightening. I'm frightened. Be frightened! |
| REBECCA | You're crazy. Dad said so. |
| MARTHA | Rebecca, listen! |
| REBECCA | You're hurting my arm. |
| MARTHA | I'm sorry, I'm sorry. How can I show you? |
| TONY | What about school? |
| MARTHA | There are signs, symbols, meanings – a fish, drowned. |
| TONY | Is this a game? |
| REBECCA | Yes. |
| MARTHA | No! My dream was a warning. Rebecca? |

*She takes off her dressing gown and puts on a mac, wellington boots and hat.*

| | |
|---|---|
| TONY | Where are you going? I want to come. Mum? |
| MARTHA | No, stay here with Rebecca. You'll be safe here, for a while. |
| TONY | Safe from what? What's going on? |
| MARTHA | From the floods. We're on high ground. |
| TONY | I don't want you to go. Mum? |
| MARTHA | Rebecca, you'll have to look after Tony. |
| REBECCA | Why? |
| MARTHA | Because that would be kind. |
| REBECCA | I've got school. |
| MARTHA | Forget school, both of you. There's no school. |
| TONY | Mum, I'm frightened. |
| MARTHA | I know. I'm going to take care of us. |
| REBECCA | Where are you going? |

10

| | |
|---|---|
| **MARTHA** | There's some things I must do, if I can. Trust me? Look after Tony. |
| **REBECCA** | No! I'm not looking after him. This is stupid. I wish I could run away. I will run away and I'll never come back. |

**Tony** *cries.*

| | |
|---|---|
| **MARTHA** | Rebecca. |
| **REBECCA** | You should see a doctor, that's what Dad said. Dad always tells the truth, always. |
| **MARTHA** | Rebecca! (*She points to* **Tony** *and hugs him.*) |
| **REBECCA** | It's your fault. |

*Silence.*

| | |
|---|---|
| **MARTHA** | I know it's hard to believe, but it's true. There will be a flood, and everything will be drowned, but we have a chance to save ourselves, because we know what's going to happen. Now there is something you can do. Tony? (*She fetches three rucksacks.*) While I'm out, I want you to pack everything into these rucksacks, everything that you'd need, that you couldn't do without if – if you were going on a camping holiday, to Cornwall. Things for a long journey. Think of it as a game. |
| **TONY** | Are we going on a long journey? |
| **MARTHA** | Maybe. |
| **REBECCA** | Don't you think you should 'phone the school – and tell them. Tell Mrs Lewis, I won't be in for science because the world's going to end. |
| **MARTHA** | Don't go out of the house. I'll be back soon. Later. (*She kisses* **Tony** *but* **Rebecca** *refuses to be kissed*). I love you both. |

*Exit* **Martha.**

# SCENE 4 • GERALD'S DAY

| | |
|---|---|
| **TONY** | What are we going to do? |
| **REBECCA** | Nothing. |
| **TONY** | Look at the rain. |
| **REBECCA** | Get away from the window. |
| **TONY** | What if it's true? What if it never stops raining? |
| **REBECCA** | It isn't true – don't be stupid. |
| **TONY** | No wind, just straight lines of water. |
| **REBECCA** | I told you not to look. (*She pulls him away roughly.*) |
| **TONY** | I'll get you back. |
| **REBECCA** | Like when? |
| **TONY** | When I'm older. |
| **REBECCA** | You're not going to be older, because the water is going to come and get you. |
| **TONY** | You said it wasn't true. |

*Silence.*

| | |
|---|---|
| **REBECCA** | (*looking out of the window*) It can't be true. It can't be. |
| **TONY** | Everything's different today, isn't it? |
| **REBECCA** | It's make-believe. It's pretend. |

**Tony** *opens the toy cupboard. Its contents spill over the stage. He puts one or two items into his rucksack.*

| | |
|---|---|
| **TONY** | Mum said that we should fill our rucksacks. |
| **REBECCA** | What for? |
| **TONY** | I don't know – (*remembers*) for a long journey. Are we going on a long journey to Cornwall? |
| **REBECCA** | She said to take things we would need, not toys. |
| **TONY** | I need my toys. I'll take my power ball, and my space gun, and the red car. I need my red car, and my clown. I'll take my frisbee. |

| REBECCA | That's my frisbee. |

*He gives it to her.*

| | I don't want it. |
| TONY | Can I take it then? |
| REBECCA | No. It's mine. I'll take my calculator, and a torch, and a radio, and my dancing shoes. |
| TONY | I'll take my baseball, my fire engine, my spacecraft. |
| REBECCA | You've got too many things. |
| TONY | And my Masters of the Universe. |
| REBECCA | Stop it. |
| TONY | And my football. |
| REBECCA | Tony. *(She grabs the football. They fight over it.)* |
| TONY | *(crying)* I want to take my football. |

*There is a silence followed by a roll of thunder which stops the two in their tracks.*

| TONY | Rebecca? Rebecca? |
| REBECCA | It's thunder. Haven't you heard thunder before? |

*There is another longer roll of thunder.* **Tony** *covers his ears and shouts.*

| TONY | Go away! Go away! Go away! |

*The lights go off.*

| REBECCA | Tony? |
| TONY | I don't want to play, I don't want to play. |
| REBECCA | Where are you? |
| TONY | Turn the light on. Rebecca? |
| REBECCA | It's all right. I'm here, I'm here. |
| TONY | Turn the light on. |
| REBECCA | I didn't turn it off – just stay still. *(She switches on the torch.)* |
| TONY | What is it? |
| REBECCA | It's a power cut, haven't you been in a power cut before? Just sit still. The lights will come back on any second. |

*Silence.*

| | |
|---|---|
| **TONY** | Why is it dark? It's daytime. |
| **REBECCA** | I don't know. How should I know? |

*She shines the light round the room. It falls on the figure of a man. They scream.* **Gerald** *shields his face.*

| | |
|---|---|
| **REBECCA** | It's Dad! It's Dad! |
| **TONY** | Dad? |
| **GERALD** | (*absent-mindedly*) Yes, yes. |
| **TONY** | We were scared. There was thunder (*stretching his hands wide*) as big as this. |
| **GERALD** | Thunder. |
| **REBECCA** | And a power cut. |
| **TONY** | But why is it dark? It's daytime isn't it? |
| **REBECCA** | Why aren't you at work? |
| **GERALD** | I – I – the rain. |
| **TONY** | Did you get my goldfish? (**Gerald** *shakes his head.*) You promised. |
| **REBECCA** | What's the matter? |
| **GERALD** | It was terrible, terrible. I got the train to go to work. The 7.45, as normal, and, and the train reached the river, and when half the train was over the bridge – the bridge collapsed into the river, which was raging, and swollen because, because of the rain. The front carriages fell into the water, and, and I was in the last carriage today, because I was late and jumped into the last carriage. If I hadn't jumped into the last carriage I – I . . . I and some other passengers climbed out onto the river bank and looked down. There were people in the water, trying to reach the bank, but they couldn't swim because they were too heavy, with briefcases, and coats and umbrellas, and they wouldn't let go of their things and the water swept them away – all floating away, newspapers, books, hats, coats, briefcases, (*pause*) people, just floating away. |
| **REBECCA** | Couldn't you save them? |

**Gerald** *looks at her sensing her reproach.*

| | |
|---|---|
| GERALD | I – walked home. |
| TONY | Then it's true, it isn't going to stop raining. |
| GERALD | Of course it will stop raining. There will be floods. Then the rain will stop, the clouds will roll back. The sun will come out and everything will return to normal. I promise. I promise. |

*The lights come on. They cheer.*

You see, everything's returning to normal.

*The lights reveal* **Martha** *standing in the room with two heavy carrier bags of provisions.*

| | |
|---|---|
| MARTHA | Gerald – you're back. |
| GERALD | Where have you been? |
| MARTHA | That's good – that's good. |
| GERALD | The children were – alone – frightened. |
| MARTHA | I've been shopping. |
| GERALD | Shopping? Shopping? |

*She begins to transfer the provisions into a rucksack.*

| | |
|---|---|
| MARTHA | Did you do as I said? Pack your things? |
| TONY | Yes. |
| REBECCA | Dad nearly drowned. |
| TONY | In a train. |
| MARTHA | (*continuing to work*) What? |
| REBECCA | A bridge collapsed. |
| TONY | And the train fell in the water. |
| REBECCA | And the people were washed away. |
| TONY | With their newspapers. |
| REBECCA | And hats and coats and cases. |
| TONY | And umbrellas. |
| MARTHA | That's terrible. Gerald – you believe me now? |
| GERALD | Believe what? That it's the end of the world? A few flash floods. No, I don't. What's this? A Beginners Guide to Sailing? |
| MARTHA | Yes. |
| GERALD | Martha? |
| MARTHA | I went down to the coast, to the harbour – and – and – and – and – and . . . |

15

| | |
|---|---|
| GERALD TONY REBECCA } | (*together*) And? |
| MARTHA | I bought a boat. |
| GERALD | What? |
| MARTHA | A boat! |
| TONY | Where? Where's the boat? |
| MARTHA | Not a toy boat – a real boat. |
| TONY | Wow! A real boat? How big? |
| MARTHA | Thirty-six feet long. With an engine, and sails – if we need them. |

*Silence.*

| | |
|---|---|
| | And I've been buying provisions, food, you know, for a long journey. |
| GERALD | You bought a boat? |
| MARTHA | Yes. |
| GERALD | Thirty-six feet long? |
| MARTHA | Yes, it's – it's yellow – ish. |

*Silence.*

| | |
|---|---|
| GERALD | You bought a boat? |
| MARTHA | Yes. |

*Silence.*

| | |
|---|---|
| GERALD | A boat? |
| REBECCA TONY } | (*together, exasperated*) Yes, a boat. |
| GERALD | What with? |
| MARTHA | With our money. |
| GERALD | My money? |
| MARTHA | All the money we had, I spent on a boat, because after today there isn't going to be any need for money, but we will need a boat. Now, coats! |
| GERALD | This is crazy – hold, hold on. |
| MARTHA | No time. Put on your coats! |
| GERALD | Martha, this is serious. Take those coats off – off! Martha if this is true . . . |

16

| | |
|---|---|
| MARTHA | It's true. Put on your coats! |
| GERALD | Take them off! Martha. This is the end Martha . . . I've had enough. The Government has been on the radio, and advised – no, *ordered* everyone not to panic, to stay at home out of the rain, where it's safe. Buying a boat, is not – it's panic. |
| MARTHA | Put on your coats! |
| GERALD | Take them off! |
| TONY | Is this a game? |
| MARTHA | No. Take the rucksacks out to the car. Go on. |

*Exit* **Rebecca** *and* **Tony**.

| | |
|---|---|
| GERALD | That's it. That is it. My solicitor will see your solicitor. |
| MARTHA | We have the same solicitor. |
| GERALD | Then he can talk to himself! But I will have the children because you are quite clearly unfit to bring them up. You have lost every right to be their mother. You have lost every screw, every marble in your tiny head – you – you – you . . . |
| MARTHA | Gerald, we have to set sail before the flood reaches its peak. There will be tidal waves, buildings collapsing. There will be terror. We must leave now. Car keys. |

*They both see them on the kitchen table and race for them.* **Gerald** *gets them.*

| | |
|---|---|
| MARTHA | I need the car. |
| GERALD | You don't need a car. You've got a boat. |
| MARTHA | It's three miles. It's pouring with rain. |
| GERALD | Walk. It'll soak some sense into you. |

*Enter* **Tony** *and* **Rebecca**.

| | |
|---|---|
| GERALD | I will never forgive you for this. For frightening our children. |

*He exits and returns an instant later with the rucksacks which he throws on the floor.*

Do you know how hard I worked for this family? (*to the children*) I'm sleeping at my mother's

17

tonight – you kids can come with me, or stay with
– with *her*.

Tony *and* Rebecca *look at each other.*

| | |
|---|---|
| **TONY** | Dad? |
| **REBECCA** | It's still raining, Dad. |
| **GERALD** | Right! Right. |

*Exit* **Gerald.**

| | |
|---|---|
| **REBECCA** | Dad, Dad, come back. Come back. (*turning on* **Martha**) I hate you. I hate you. |
| **TONY** | I knew this wasn't a game. I just knew. |
| **MARTHA** | Put on your rucksacks. We have to walk. |
| **TONY** | Will we see Dad again? |
| **MARTHA** | (*pause*) I – (*roll of thunder*) We have to hurry. Say goodbye to the house. |
| **TONY** | What about Grandma and Grandad – what about . . . |
| **MARTHA** | Later, Tony. Later. Say goodbye to the house first. |
| **TONY** | Goodbye, house. |
| **MARTHA** | Becky? (**Rebecca** *looks away.*) Goodbye, house. |

*Blackout.*

| | |
|---|---|
| **CHORUS** | The rain ran down the face of the earth into its gaping mouth, filling its head to overflow. |
| | The sullen rivers brown and muddy grew, from weaklings into giants, with muscles mighty of their own, their boundaries and banks they overleapt. |
| | On and on the water came, with rage and roar, over farms and ancient battlefields it fled, sweeping away the gentle villages of our history. |

On and on the water came
toward the market towns
where businessmen have bartered
and bled and buried their dead,
row upon row.

On and on the water came,
even the army boys
whose bravery is brought to bear
on such occasions
were overwhelmed by flood;

their tanks like toys by children
pushed aside,
on and on the water came
toward the proud cathedral spires,
and all who saw the flood
had seen the day
to end all days.

On and on the water came.

# SCENE 5 • PREPARING THE BOAT

*The silhouette of the city on the backcloth fades. The house, or the few items that have constituted the house have been removed. As the lights rise we see* **Martha**, **Tony** *and* **Rebecca**, *on the quay. A gangplank goes up to a raised area. They are loading the boat.* **Rebecca** *is on the top.* **Martha** *below has a checklist.*

| | |
|---|---|
| **MARTHA** | Flour? |
| **REBECCA** | Yes. |
| **MARTHA** | Dried milk? |
| **REBECCA** | Yes. |
| **MARTHA** | Tinned meat? |
| **REBECCA** | Yes. (*She looks into the distance as if she's seen someone.*) |
| **MARTHA** | Any sign? |
| **REBECCA** | No – it's someone else. He's not coming. |
| **TONY** | (*who has not heard, beneath the weight of a sack*) Is he coming? |
| **REBECCA** | No, he's not, *not* – listen! |
| **MARTHA** | Dried fruit? |
| **REBECCA** | Yes. |
| **MARTHA** | Salt? |
| **REBECCA** | Yes. |
| **MARTHA** | Sugar? |
| **REBECCA** | Yes. |
| **MARTHA** | Water, yes. Right then – this lot. Matches? |
| **REBECCA** | Yes. |
| **MARTHA** | Life jackets? Four? |
| **REBECCA** | Yes. |
| **MARTHA** | Blankets? |
| **REBECCA** | Yes. |
| **MARTHA** | Rope? |
| **REBECCA** | Yes. |

| | |
|---|---|
| **MARTHA** | Torches? |
| **REBECCA** | Yes. |
| **MARTHA** | Knives? |
| **REBECCA** | Look! Look! Look! |
| **TONY** | Is it Dad? |
| **REBECCA** | No, it's a break in the cloud. I can see a blue patch. |

*They stare up. Suddenly a brilliant shaft of sunlight hits* **Rebecca.** *The others cheer. Then it slowly fades.*

| | |
|---|---|
| **TONY** | (*shouting at the sky*) Come back. Come back. |
| **MARTHA** | Rebecca. (*pause*) Rebecca. |
| **REBECCA** | What? What? |
| **MARTHA** | Tin-opener? |
| **REBECCA** | Yes. |
| **MARTHA** | Bottle-opener? |
| **REBECCA** | Yes, yes, yes, yes, yes, yes, yes. |

**Rebecca** *sits, head in hands.* **Gerald** *enters, wet and battered, but still holding his briefcase.*

| | |
|---|---|
| **TONY** | Dad! (*runs up and hugs him*) |
| **REBECCA** | We thought you weren't coming. |
| **TONY** | We thought we'd never see you again. |
| **MARTHA** | You changed your mind? |

*He does not respond and they back away.*

| | |
|---|---|
| **GERALD** | I hold here in my hand, a piece of paper. The Government has issued this paper. I quote: 'This is a national emergency. *Do not*, repeat, *do not* leave your homes. Move into the upper part of the house, where you will be safe. Do not panic. The water will subside soon, and the Government will help pay for damages to property'. That is our Government. To do anything else, to buy boats, to run away is nothing more than cowardice. In fact, it's as near to treason as you can get. |
| **TONY** | What's that? |
| **GERALD** | Treason, Tony, is not doing as you're told. It's |

|           |                                                                                                 |
| --------- | ----------------------------------------------------------------------------------------------- |
|           | breaking the rules. Now both of you come home with me. We'll live in the upstairs room until the rain stops. Tony? |
| TONY      | Mum?                                                                                            |
| MARTHA    | The rain won't stop.                                                                            |
| GERALD    | The rain will stop, the Government has said so.                                                 |

**Tony** *joins his mother.*

|           |                                                                                                 |
| --------- | ----------------------------------------------------------------------------------------------- |
|           | Rebecca, I promise you if you come home your life will go on as normal. Your mother is – mistaken. She's not well. There's nothing to be afraid of. Think. Think. |
| MARTHA    | Do what you feel.                                                                               |
| REBECCA   | I hate you, both of you. (*She goes to the gangplank and sits on it.*)                          |
| GERALD    | Rebecca! Do you know what will happen to us when the Sunday papers get hold of this? 'Lunatic wife of businessman flees end of world in yellow yacht.' We'll lose everything. I'll lose my job. |
| MARTHA    | You hate your job.                                                                              |
| GERALD    | That's a lie. I love my job. I love my job.                                                     |
| TONY      | Dad, Dad.                                                                                       |
| REBECCA   | The water. It's coming. It's coming. Look!                                                      |
| MARTHA    | (*throwing up the rucksacks*) Into the boat now. Now!                                           |
| GERALD    | Ha! You're all mad.                                                                             |

**Rebecca** *lifts a hatch and drops the rucksacks through. We hear the rush of water getting louder as the scene continues to a climax.*

|                    |                                                                           |
| ------------------ | ------------------------------------------------------------------------- |
| TONY               | Dad, Dad, look behind you – behind you!                                    |
| MARTHA             | Gerald. Get into the boat. This is your last chance – it's a tidal wave.   |
| GERALD             | Ha!                                                                       |
| REBECCA<br>TONY    | } (*together*) Come on, come on!                                           |
| GERALD             | How dare you laugh at me.                                                  |
| MARTHA             | Gerald!                                                                    |
| GERALD             | You've betrayed me, all of you.                                           |

22

| | |
|---|---|
| **REBECCA** | *(together, pointing into the distance)* Dad. |
| **TONY** | |
| **GERALD** | I will not look. I will not look. |

**Martha** *twists* **Gerald** *round. He sees the water, behind the audience as it were, and screams.* **Tony** *and* **Rebecca** *rush down the gangplank and the three of them push him up and then down into the hatch as the sound of the water reaches a terrifying roar.* **Tony** *rushes back to pick up his father's briefcase which he dropped when he saw the tidal wave.*

**MARTHA**       Tony! Tony!

**Tony** *gets back in and as they close the hatch, the sound fades and it goes dark.* **Rebecca** *switches on a torch.*

**MARTHA**       We're afloat! We're afloat!

**Rebecca** *shines the light on her father's face, which is frozen in an expression of absolute terror and surprise. He then faints.*

# ACT TWO

## SCENE 1 • INSIDE THE BOAT

CHORUS

Down, down, the water comes.
Rivers become seas,
seas surge over land to make one sea.
The people crouch in upper rooms,
too terrified to speak.
Then the water breaks the fragile
windowpanes, and rushes in
to kill, to kill.
Before too long the nick-nacks
of our lives are floating aimlessly about
as in a dream.
Now the water runs across
the rooftops of the towns,
and still it comes, down, down, down,
until all the cities of our world
lie still and breathless far below.
Down, down, down, the water comes
until the poor birds
can find no tree, no perch,
and flop exhausted
into the sea, from which
they came, once, many lives ago,
half fish, half bird.
One by one, the hills and mountains disappear.
The cruel summits, that in their time
have scuppered those who dared to climb,
are now no more than pimples
that peak above the rage and roar.
Now there is nothing
only sky and flood;
only the ancient creatures of the deep,
older than all mankind,
older, too, than good and bad.
Now there is nothing,

only sky and flood,
and a small boat bobbing
on a salty sea.

*Lights rise. The inside of the boat. We hear the boat creaking. It is early
morning.* **Martha** *and* **Gerald** *are asleep on one side of the stage and on
the other* **Tony** *and* **Rebecca** *are sleeping. They are in sleeping bags.
Next to them are life jackets, and wellington boots. They sleep with their
clothes on. It is still raining.*

| | |
|---|---|
| **TONY** | Becky? Rebecca? Are you awake? (*He shines his torch in her face.*) |
| **REBECCA** | No. |
| **TONY** | I can't sleep. I was thinking about all the people we left behind. Grandma and Grandad. |
| **REBECCA** | Tony, you promised. |
| **TONY** | But I can't help it. I keep seeing their faces, don't you? Becky, don't you? |
| **REBECCA** | Yes. |
| **TONY** | Aunty Jane and Uncle George. All our schoolfriends – Skippy, Mike, Peter. And Miss Lewis and Mr Hardcastle. They can't be drowned, can they? |
| **REBECCA** | They must be. |
| **TONY** | Even Brown Owl? |

*She comforts him.*

| | |
|---|---|
| **TONY** | It's not fair, it's not fair. |
| **REBECCA** | There must be some other people alive. People who survived the flood just like we did. |
| **TONY** | Who? |
| **REBECCA** | People who were at sea, on boats. Sailors, and people. |
| **TONY** | We'll join up with them won't we? (*She nods.*) I knew we would, I just knew. |

**Gerald** *gets up.*

| | |
|---|---|
| **TONY** | What's that? |
| **REBECCA** | Ssh. (*She gets up and looks, and comes back.*) It's only Dad. |

| | |
|---|---|
| **TONY** | What's he doing? |
| **REBECCA** | Walking up and down. |
| **TONY** | Is that bad? |
| **REBECCA** | Ssh. Just listen |

**Martha** *sits up.*

| | |
|---|---|
| **MARTHA** | Gerald, what time is it? |
| **GERALD** | Nearly morning. |

**Martha** *sits up, half awake.*

| | |
|---|---|
| **GERALD** | Thoughts, pictures, going round and round in my head. The office is underwater – all the desks, computers, 'phones, files, all floating about. I was about to be rich. Now all the money is just – floating about, like us, floating endlessly on and on. |
| **TONY** | What? |
| **REBECCA** | Ssh – I can't hear. |
| **GERALD** | Forty days. |
| **MARTHA** | Gerald . . . |
| **GERALD** | And forty nights we've been floating, drifting. |
| **TONY** | What? |
| **GERALD** | The kids have been great. |
| **REBECCA** | He says we were late. |
| **TONY** | What for? |
| **GERALD** | I thought they were selfish. |
| **REBECCA** | He thought we were shellfish. |
| **TONY** | What? |
| **GERALD** | What's going to happen to us, Martha? |
| **MARTHA** | (*tetchy*) I don't know. Why should I know more than anyone else? |
| **GERALD** | Martha, the things I said before the flood . . . |
| **MARTHA** | Gone, all gone. (*She kisses him.*) |
| **TONY** | What's happening? |
| **REBECCA** | They're kissing. |
| **TONY** | Ugh! |
| **REBECCA** | Do you know what that means? |
| **TONY** | Another baby? |
| **REBECCA** | No. Don't be silly. (*She tickles him and he laughs.*) |
| **GERALD** | Hey, you two, go to sleep. |

| | |
|---|---|
| **REBECCA** | Please. |
| **GERALD** | Please. Goodnight sweethearts. |
| **REBECCA** | Goodnight Rubberlips. |

*They giggle.* **Martha** *and* **Gerald** *settle down.*

| | |
|---|---|
| **REBECCA** | I'm hungry. |
| **TONY** | I've got a hole in my stomach, (*stretching his hands wide*) this big. |
| **REBECCA** | Come on, be quiet though. |

*They come to the front of the stage.* **Rebecca** *filches some biscuits. She has her torch.*

| | |
|---|---|
| **REBECCA** | What? |
| **TONY** | It's still raining. If it doesn't stop we'll die, here on the boat, won't we? |

**Rebecca** *nods.*

| | |
|---|---|
| **TONY** | Becky? Why did it happen? Why did the world end? Why is everyone we ever knew dead? |
| **REBECCA** | I don't know. |
| **TONY** | Is it a punishment? Were we bad? I wasn't bad, was I? |
| **REBECCA** | No. |
| **TONY** | I've never done anything really bad. I've never killed anyone. I've never killed anything on purpose. Not even an ant. Have you? |

*Pause.*

| | |
|---|---|
| **REBECCA** | Yes. |
| **TONY** | What? |
| **REBECCA** | I killed your goldfish– on the night before the flood. I overfed it. |
| **TONY** | On purpose? |
| **REBECCA** | Yes. |
| **TONY** | (*more curious than angry*) Why? |
| **REBECCA** | I don't know, I don't know. |
| **TONY** | Is *that* why the world ended? |

27

| | |
|---|---|
| **REBECCA** | No, of course not. |
| **TONY** | Then why? |
| **REBECCA** | I don't know! Does there have to be a reason? |
| **TONY** | Dad says there's a reason for everything. |

*Silence.*

| | |
|---|---|
| **REBECCA** | Listen. |
| **TONY** | What? |
| **REBECCA** | Listen. |
| **TONY** | I can't hear anything. |
| **REBECCA** | Nothing? You hear nothing? Not even the rain. |

*They jump up in excitement.*

| | |
|---|---|
| | Mum! Mum! |
| **TONY** | Dad! Dad! |
| **GERALD** | (*coming out of a dream*) What – no – time. What? What? Who? Tony – what? |
| **TONY** | It's stopped raining. It's stopped raining. (*shaking his mother*) Mum, Mum, it's stopped raining! Wake up! Wake up! |

*They get dressed in boots and life jackets.* **Martha** *is exhausted and follows slowly. They go out onto the deck as it were.*

# SCENE 2 • THE TORNADO

| | |
|---|---|
| **GERALD** | Ha! Ha! It has. It's stopped raining. |
| **REBECCA** | Look! The sun, I can see the sun. |

*They are grouped very close together and are suddenly bathed in a shaft of light as in Act One. The image should be identical.*

| | |
|---|---|
| **TONY** | Please don't go away this time. Please stay. |

*The light gets stronger.* **Martha** *smiles weakly.*

| | |
|---|---|
| | Mum, it's stopped raining. |
| **MARTHA** | Yes. |
| **REBECCA** | That's hopeful isn't it? |
| **MARTHA** | Yes, it is hopeful. |
| **REBECCA** | The water will go down. |
| **TONY** | And we'll find land, won't we? |
| **MARTHA** | Maybe, maybe. |

*A gentle wind starts to blow, then suddenly gathers speed and noise.*

| | |
|---|---|
| **GERALD** | What now? |
| **REBECCA** | Look, over there, across the sea. |
| **TONY** | What is it? |
| **GERALD** | It's a windstorm. A tornado. |

*They stand open-mouthed for a moment.*

| | |
|---|---|
| | (*whispers*) God of Gods. |
| **MARTHA** | Everyone below deck! |

**Tony** *stares in wonder.*

| | |
|---|---|
| **GERALD** | Come on, Tony, move! Move! |
| **TONY** | I want to see. I want to see. |

*His father drags him down below.* **Martha** *pulls in the rope.*

**GERALD**      Martha! Martha!

*The wind sound reaches a terrible scream and howl, as they close the hatch and huddle in a close group. Lights change.*

**CHORUS**      The clouds curl back at the corners,
and the rain ceases to rule.
Then comes the dry wind,
screaming over the wet skin of the world,
howling like a hungry wolf, it blows,
muscle of air, sinew of breath,
tunnel of twisting rage.
What the rain could not destroy,
the burning breath of ancient gods
blows asunder.

*The noise fades to silence.*

**GERALD**      It's over, passed on.

*The boat is now creaking heavily.*

**REBECCA**      What's that sound?
**MARTHA**      Gerald?
**GERALD**      I'll check the hold.
**MARTHA**      Tony, help me.

*They go on deck, and pull on to centre stage a small dinghy as in* **Martha's** *dream in Act One.*

**TONY**      Are we sinking?
**MARTHA**      The wind may have broken the fibreglass. Get your things together. Hurry! Rebecca, you hear?

*They scurry about, filling their rucksacks.*

**GERALD**      (*entering*) We've sprung a leak. We've got to get out – out – out. Now!
**REBECCA**      How long?
**GERALD**      Three minutes if that.
**TONY**      What?
**GERALD**      We're sinking, Tony, that's what! Up and out!
**MARTHA**      Gerald, the water. Tony, sleeping bags. Rebecca, life jackets.

# SCENE 3 • THE DINGHY

*They pull on the life jackets, as they climb the stairs, all shouting.*
*Everything is in complete chaos. They jump into the dinghy. The raised*
*area disappears from view, leaving a clear image of boat against*
*backcloth.*

| | |
|---|---|
| **TONY** | Look! She's sinking. Our boat's sinking! |
| **GERALD** | Don't stand up. You'll fall in. |
| **TONY** | But our boat – it's gone! It was there, just there on the water, and now it's gone! |
| **MARTHA** | Sit down, Tony. Sit down! |

*Silence.*

| | |
|---|---|
| **CHORUS** | After the rain came the wind. After the wind came the sun, beating the back of the world with strokes of fire, strokes of fire. |

*As the Chorus speaks, the 'sun' rises to its highest.*

| | |
|---|---|
| **REBECCA** | There's water coming in over the side. |
| **MARTHA** | We've too many things on board. All we need are clothes, food and water. |

*She reaches for **Tony's** rucksack. He pulls it back.*

| | |
|---|---|
| | Everything else is useless – over the side! |
| **TONY** | No! |
| **MARTHA** | What's in there? |
| **TONY** | My things. |
| **MARTHA** | What *things*? |
| **TONY** | What about *her* things? |
| **MARTHA** | Gerald, will you help me? |
| **GERALD** | What – now? |

| | |
|---|---|
| **MARTHA** | Rebecca – you first. |
| **REBECCA** | Why me? |
| **MARTHA** | I don't know why *me* – why anyone? |

**Gerald** *nods to* **Rebecca,** *sensing that* **Martha** *has had enough.*
**Rebecca** *opens her rucksack and, one by one, discards the items in a ritual farewell.*

| | |
|---|---|
| **REBECCA** | My calculator, my frisbee, my skipping rope, my . . . can't I keep my dancing shoes? |
| **MARTHA** | You've no need for them. (*She throws them over.*) Tony. |
| **TONY** | My frisbee, my power ball, my space gun, my red car, my ambulance, my Masters of the Universe, my football, my . . . can't I keep my clown? I've had him since I was – this big. |
| **MARTHA** | It wouldn't be fair. |

*He throws it overboard, and they drift away as the scenes continue. They turn to* **Gerald** *who is clutching his briefcase.*

| | |
|---|---|
| **MARTHA** | Gerald? |
| **GERALD** | What about you? |
| **MARTHA** | (*bitterly*) I brought nothing. I had nothing. The briefcase. |
| **GERALD** | No, I can't. There are important things in here – vital to our survival. |
| **MARTHA** | What things? |
| **GERALD** | The water's not coming in any more – see. |
| **REBECCA** | You've got to throw it away. |
| **TONY** | It's your turn. I threw away my clown. |
| **GERALD** | No, I must keep this. I must. |
| **MARTHA** | Gerald. |

*She reaches for it and they struggle as in Act One.*

| | |
|---|---|
| **REBECCA** | Don't fight. Don't fight! |

**Martha** *pulls away, very upset and more exhausted than ever.*

| | |
|---|---|
| **TONY** | Mum, are you all right? |
| **MARTHA** | Oh, fine. Mothers are always *just fine.* |

| | |
|---|---|
| **REBECCA** | You should throw it overboard. |
| **TONY** | It's not fair. |
| **GERALD** | I'm your father. |
| **REBECCA** | So? |
| **GERALD** | And I say this briefcase stays with me. Let that be an end to it. An end! |

*Silence. The sun shines hotter.*

| | |
|---|---|
| **TONY** | How much water have we got? |
| **REBECCA** | Enough for a week. |
| **TONY** | It's so hot. Are we going to die? |
| **GERALD** | No! |
| **REBECCA** | Not for a week . . . |
| **GERALD** | That's enough! |

*Silence.*

| | |
|---|---|
| **TONY** | Can I have some water? |
| **REBECCA** | Mum? |
| **MARTHA** | One cup, per person, per day. |
| **TONY** | Is that all? |
| **MARTHA** | That's all. Rebecca? |

**Rebecca** *gives them a drink each.*

| | |
|---|---|
| **GERALD** | (*to* **Martha** *but she has already collapsed*) Try and get some sleep. |

*The lights change.*

| | |
|---|---|
| **CHORUS** | After the rain |
| | came the wind. |
| | After the wind |
| | came the sun, |
| | beating the back of the world |
| | with strokes of fire, |
| | strokes of fire. |

*The lights rise.*

| | |
|---|---|
| **REBECCA** | Look, over there in the water. |

| TONY | What is it? |
| MARTHA | It's a bird – a dead bird. |
| GERALD | Can you reach it? |
| REBECCA | No, it's too far. It's gone. It's gone. |

*Rebecca, Martha and Gerald react to this in a way Tony cannot understand.*

| TONY | What's the matter? Becky? |
| REBECCA | It means we're . . . |
| GERALD | Don't worry him. |
| TONY | I want to know. |

*Martha nods at Rebecca.*

| REBECCA | It means we're a long way from land. The bird flew as far as it could, found no land, and fell into the water. |
| GERALD | It's time. |

*Rebecca pours out a drink for each of them.*

| TONY | You've got more than me. |
| REBECCA | No, I haven't. |
| TONY | I can see. I can see. It's not fair. |
| MARTHA | Gerald. |
| TONY | I want some more. |
| GERALD | We have to share it, make it last as long as possible. |
| TONY | But I'm thirsty, I'm thirsty! |

*Silence.*

| REBECCA | You can finish mine. |

*She offers it. He takes it and is about to drink, then gives it back. He lowers his head.*

| TONY | I'm frightened. |

*Rebecca comforts him. Lights change.*

34

| CHORUS | After the rain<br>came the wind.<br>After the wind<br>came the sun,<br>beating the back of the world<br>with strokes of fire,<br>strokes of fire. |
|---|---|

*Lights rise. On the backcloth appears a silhouette of a dove.*

| GERALD | Look in the sky. There! Martha, look! There's a bird in the sky. Martha! Martha? |
|---|---|
| REBECCA | What's the matter? |
| GERALD | Some water. Give her some water. |
| TONY | Mum? Mum, we saw a bird. |

**Gerald** *tries to give her some water, but only a few drops come out.*

| GERALD | Martha, the bird had a stick in it's mouth. It's building a nest, somewhere near – on land. Martha. Martha. |
|---|---|
| MARTHA | (*very weak*) My dream. My dream. The rain, the wind, the sea, the boat, the birds, the tree, the tree. |

*She collapses over the side of the dinghy, as in the opening image of the play.*

| GERALD | She's exhausted. It's my fault. (*holding his head in his hands*) Get some sleep, if you can. |
|---|---|

*They sit back, and all sleep. The lights change and there is the sound of waves breaking, getting stronger. In a surreal fashion, a single tree bearing apples is rolled on upstage. The sound of waves dies down, and there is a soft, strange music which wakes* **Tony.**

| TONY | Dad, Dad, wake up! Rebecca! Mum! Wake up! We're on land. We're on land! |
|---|---|

*Gerald sits up.* **Rebecca** *and* **Tony** *step out.*

| GERALD | Martha, Martha. We've found land. We're safe. We're safe. Tony, Rebecca. |
|---|---|

*They lift* **Martha** *from the dinghy which is dragged upstage.*

| | |
|---|---|
| **REBECCA** | Is she still alive? |
| **GERALD** | See if there's some fresh water close by. Hurry, hurry! |
| **TONY** | Where are we? |
| **GERALD** | I don't know. It'll be night soon. We'll sleep here on the beach. |
| **TONY** | I heard music, did you? |
| **GERALD** | I heard something. I thought I was dreaming. |

**Rebecca** *brings water to* **Martha**. **Gerald** *makes her drink. She lies with her head on* **Gerald's** *lap. The children kneel either side, forming a tableau as the lights fade and the music gathers strength.*

| | |
|---|---|
| **TONY** | Mum, we're here! We've arrived! Mum? |

*Lights fade to blackout, as if the sun finally sinks on their ordeal at sea.*

# SCENE 4 • THE ISLAND

*vening. An orange sun on the backcloth, rises and falls during the scene*
*s if a complete day passes during the action.* **Martha** *is asleep*
*nderneath the tree. She has been exhausted by the whole trip and has*
*?en asleep for a few days. As the lights rise* **Tony** *puts a cold wet cloth on*
*?r forehead. There is strange music which fades as* **Rebecca** *enters.*

| | |
|---|---|
| EBECCA | Is she awake? |
| ONY | No. What if she never wakes up? Just goes on sleeping? |
| EBECCA | She'll wake up. Look. |
| ONY | Wow? What are they, jewels? |
| EBECCA | I don't think so. Stones, shiny stones. |
| ONY | Where did you find them? |
| EBECCA | In the lake. They stayed shiny even when I dried them. |
| ONY | I think they're jewels. We could make something – a shape. |
| EBECCA | A circle. |
| ONY | A magic circle. Can I come in? |
| EBECCA | Yes, but only if you . . . (*thinking*) |
| ONY | Make a secret sign like this. (*He makes a sign and she mirrors it.*) And then tell a secret. |
| EBECCA | No, not a secret – not here. You ask a question and I have to tell the truth. In this circle you have to tell the truth. That's the game. |
| ONY | Easy. (*pausing*) You start. |
| EBECCA | What's your favourite colour? |
| ONY | Red. |
| EBECCA | Your turn. |
| ONY | What's your favourite food? |
| EBECCA | Before it was chips, now it's those star-shaped yellow fruits with the purple centre. |
| ONY | Disgusting. |
| EBECCA | What do you miss most from before? |

| TONY | People. Don't you ever feel lonely here? It's so quiet. |
| REBECCA | Is that your question? (*He nods.*) Yes, sometimes, a bit. |
| TONY | A big bit? |
| REBECCA | It's my turn. What do you like most about the island? |

**Tony** *shrugs.*

| | Which part? The forest? The lake? The mountains? |
| TONY | The river. I like the river. You can *see* the fish. |
| REBECCA | Your turn. |
| TONY | You said God was make-believe, like Father Christmas. Is that true? |
| REBECCA | About God? |
| TONY | No, about Father Christmas. Is he make-believe? |
| REBECCA | What do you think? |

**Tony** *lowers his head.*

| TONY | Is God make-believe, too? |
| REBECCA | I'm not sure – but if he is real, I bet he lives on an island just like this one. |
| TONY | (*restored to happiness*) Yeah. Your question. |
| REBECCA | If you could make one wish in the world, what would it be? |
| TONY | (*pause*) I'd – I'd  go back to how it was before the rain and make it not happen. |
| REBECCA | Your turn. |
| TONY | Why did you kill my goldfish? |
| REBECCA | (*pause*) I wanted to hurt you. |
| TONY | I found a pool in the forest which is full of goldfish, (*stretching his arms as wide as they can go*) this big. |
| REBECCA | Can I see them? |
| TONY | Come on. (*He runs straight off, leaving* **Rebecca** *stunned.*) |

| | |
|---|---|
| REBECCA | Wait for me. |

**Martha** *is awake.*

| | |
|---|---|
| MARTHA | Rebecca? |
| REBECCA | Mum? Mum? |
| MARTHA | Where are we? |
| REBECCA | It's all right, everything's all right. You're safe. Tony! Tony! |
| MARTHA | We were at sea. |
| REBECCA | You collapsed, fell asleep and we found this island. |
| MARTHA | I'm so thirsty. (*She drinks and it has an immediate effect.*) |
| REBECCA | The water's different – everything's different here. |

**Martha** *sits up. She then hides her face in her hands.*

What's wrong, Mum?

**Martha** *embraces* **Rebecca**.

| | |
|---|---|
| MARTHA | No, nothing. I just thought – we're alive – and I – well – it doesn't matter what I thought. |
| REBECCA | You saved us. |

*Enter* **Tony**.

| | |
|---|---|
| TONY | Mum, Mum, are you feeling better? |
| MARTHA | (*surprised*) Yes. |
| REBECCA | It's the water – it's special. |
| MARTHA | How long have I been asleep? |
| TONY | Three days. Dad said it was stress. (*They help her up.*) I said you were just fed up. |
| MARTHA | Where is he? |
| REBECCA | Gone fishing. |
| TONY | Are you hungry? |
| MARTHA | Yes I . . . |
| TONY | Have this – it's disgusting. |
| REBECCA | It's not, it's my favourite. (*She eats some fruit.*) See. |

| | |
|---|---|
| **MARTHA** | Is there anyone else on the island? |
| **REBECCA** | No one. |
| **TONY** | Apart from the animals. |

*As the next section develops. The children begin to run around, and it develops into a loose dance as they talk. It is a free expression of their feelings.*

| | |
|---|---|
| **TONY** | Every kind of animal you ever heard of. |
| **REBECCA** | And lots more. Apes. |
| **TONY** | Antelope. |
| **REBECCA** | Bears. |
| **TONY** | Badgers. |
| **REBECCA** | Cats. |
| **TONY** | Cows. |
| **REBECCA** | Deer. |
| **TONY** | Donkeys. |
| **REBECCA** | Elephants. |
| **TONY** | Emus. |
| **REBECCA** | Foxes. |
| **TONY** | Frogs. |
| **REBECCA** | Giraffes. |
| **TONY** | Geese. |
| **REBECCA** | Hippos. |
| **TONY** | Horses. |
| **REBECCA** | Lions. |
| **TONY** | Leopards. |
| **REBECCA** | Monkeys. |
| **TONY** | Moles. |
| **REBECCA** | Rats. |
| **TONY** | Rabbits – hundreds. |
| **REBECCA** | Tigers. |
| **TONY** | Tarantulas. |
| **REBECCA** | Wildebeest. |
| **TONY** | Wolves. |
| **REBECCA** | Yetis. |
| **TONY** | And zebra. |
| **MARTHA** | Do these animals walk around in alphabetical order? |

| | |
|---|---|
| REBECCA | (*laughing*) No that was just a game. |
| TONY | We've had so much time to play games. These are the truth stones. |
| REBECCA | This is just the beach part. Over there is a forest. |
| TONY | A wonderful forest. |
| REBECCA | Greener than green. |
| TONY | Deeper than deep. |
| REBECCA | Full of monkeys and birds. |
| TONY | You should see the colours of the birds. Yellow and red. |
| REBECCA | Purple and orange. |
| TONY | Red and green. |
| REBECCA | Birds like – like traffic lights. |

*They laugh and run around spinning and jumping.*

|  | And there are strange animals, too. |
|---|---|
| TONY | Which are half bird. |
| REBECCA | Half animal – that we've never seen before. |
| TONY | Not even in books. |
| REBECCA | And there's food in the forest. |
| TONY | Fruit. |
| REBECCA | Vegetables. |
| TONY | Nuts. |
| REBECCA | And, and – all growing wild. It's more like an orchard. |
| TONY | More like a garden. |
| REBECCA | Than a forest. |
| TONY | And over here is a lake. |
| REBECCA | Such a beautiful lake. It's bluer than blue. |
| TONY | Wider than wide. |
| REBECCA | Wetter than wet. |

*They laugh and run again.*

|  | And up there are the mountains, with snow on the peaks – higher than high. |
|---|---|
| TONY | Cleaner than clean. |
| REBECCA | Whiter than white. |

| TONY | Like – like washing powder. |

*They laugh and run again to another place.*

| REBECCA | And over there is a plain which stretches for miles. |
| TONY | With a long winding river full of fish. |
| REBECCA | And there's herds of deer, buffaloes, antelope. |
| TONY | And wild pigs – it's brilliant. |
| REBECCA | It's beautiful and every night as the sun sets, and every morning as the sun rises, we hear this strange music. (*She dances.*) |
| TONY | We've looked and looked but we can't find where it comes from. |
| REBECCA | I don't want to find out where it comes from. That would spoil it. |
| MARTHA | And you're sure there's no one else on the island? |
| TONY | No one. |
| REBECCA | Just us. |
| TONY | For ever and ever. Just us. |
| REBECCA | (*holding up the briefcase*) And look what I found. |
| MARTHA | That's not yours, Rebecca. |
| REBECCA | He tried to hide it – under a rock. |
| TONY | But we searched everywhere. |
| REBECCA | He said it would help us survive. |
| TONY | I want to see what's inside. |
| REBECCA | So do I. Don't you? |

**Martha** *nods and they kneel round the briefcase and open it. They pull out sheet after sheet of paper.* **Gerald** *enters unseen.*

| TONY | It's nothing – just paper. |
| REBECCA | It's got writing on it. |
| TONY | What does it say? Does it say why the world ended? |
| GERALD | No. |

*They stand back as* **Gerald** *comes forward and kneels in front of the briefcase.*

| MARTHA | What are they? |

| | |
|---|---|
| **GERALD** | Plans. Plans for new buildings, houses, hotels, hospitals, holiday homes, retirement homes, offices. Plans for the future development of the world. The old world. |
| **REBECCA** | Why did you bring them? |
| **GERALD** | I thought, perhaps it was all a nightmare, and that I'd suddenly wake up and need all these plans. Stupid, I know. It wasn't logical. They're useless now, aren't they? |
| **TONY** | No. (*He has made a paper aeroplane.*) We can make paper planes. |
| **REBECCA** | And paper hats. |
| **TONY** | And paper chains. |
| **REBECCA** | And paper dolls. |
| **TONY** | We can use it as toilet paper. |
| **REBECCA**<br>**TONY** | } (*together*) Paper, paper, paper, paper, paper. |

*The two children throw the paper into the air.* **Martha** *and* **Gerald** *embrace. Lights fade, as the sun sets and the strange music plays.*

# SCENE 5 • ANOTHER BOAT

CHORUS      The sun rose and the sun set on the new world,
            and the new world was a good world,
            serene and kind, all things in perfect measure.
            The days were long, like the best of summer days,
            the nights were soft and cool,
            and darkness came without fear.

*Soft light on* **Gerald** *and* **Martha**.

GERALD      Martha, we can build something here,
            something good. Clear a patch of land, build a
            house. I can build a pulley system to bring water
            from the river. I saw that in a film once. These
            people were castaways, and they built their own
            world, and they were happy, so happy.

*Light fades on them.*

CHORUS      The rivers and streams ran clear and clean.
            The air was fresh and full of flight.
            The earth itself was rich and strong,
            yearly renewing itself from within
            so that nothing in the new world died
            that was not reborn,
            and the knowledge of eternal life
            breathed itself into song.
            The combining elements of earth, air and water
            were instruments that played
            the gentle music of our oldest god,
            the Earth, the Earth, the Earth.

**Tony** *enters stealthily. He has a roughly made bow and arrow. He is
hunting. He pulls back the arrow and fires. Enter* **Gerald.** *He carries a
long pole on which are hung a dozen or so rabbits, covered in blood.*
**Gerald's** *hands are also covered in blood, as are* **Tony's.**

GERALD      Any luck?

44

| | |
|---|---|
| **TONY** | No. Missed again. |
| **GERALD** | You mustn't rush. Take your time. |

*Enter* **Rebecca.**

| | |
|---|---|
| **TONY** | Rebecca, look! |
| **GERALD** | Let's get a fire going. |
| **TONY** | Dad and I killed these rabbits. It was easy they just came right up to us and we hit them over the head with sticks. |
| **GERALD** | We're running out of matches. Where's Martha? |
| **TONY** | And the other rabbits didn't even run away. It was great. (*demonstrating how they killed them*) Bang! Bang! Bang! |
| **GERALD** | We'll have to find another way to make fire. |
| **TONY** | Can we go hunting again? For deer and antelope. |
| **GERALD** | Of course. We're free. We can do what we like – it's our island. (*He ruffles his son's head with affection.*) |
| **TONY** | Whoopee! |

**Tony** *dances round, a kind of war dance very different to the movements used when he and* **Rebecca** *were describing the island to* **Martha**. *He stops when he sees* **Rebecca's** *face as she kneels by the rabbits.*

| | |
|---|---|
| **TONY** | What's the matter? |
| **GERALD** | They're only rabbits, Rebecca. Just rabbits. |
| **REBECCA** | It isn't fair. |
| **GERALD** | Life isn't fair, Rebecca. Ask everyone who drowned in the flood. |
| **REBECCA** | It's horrible. |
| **GERALD** | We've got to live, Rebecca. |
| **REBECCA** | But you killed so many. |
| **GERALD** | So we had a bit of fun. What's wrong with that? |
| **REBECCA** | Murderers. |
| **GERALD** | Rebecca. |
| **REBECCA** | Murderers. |
| **GERALD** | That's enough! |

*Pause.*

| | |
|---|---|
| **REBECCA** | I'll bury them. |

| | |
|---|---|
| **GERALD** | Bury them? Rabbits? |
| **REBECCA** | The ones we can't eat. There's too many to eat. |
| **GERALD** | So bury them. See if I care. (*looking at his bloody hands*) I'm going to wash in the river. |

*Exit* **Gerald**.

| | |
|---|---|
| **TONY** | I didn't mean anything. I just followed Dad. |
| **REBECCA** | It isn't our island. It can't be. |
| **TONY** | Why not? |
| **REBECCA** | Who did it belong to before we arrived? |
| **TONY** | No one. |
| **REBECCA** | If it didn't belong to us then, it doesn't belong to us now. |
| **TONY** | Does that mean we can't do what we like? |
| **REBECCA** | Not if it's wrong. |
| **TONY** | How do you know if it's wrong? |
| **REBECCA** | You just know. We'll make a pact. A secret pact. |

*She goes into the stone circle.*

| | |
|---|---|
| **TONY** | Okay, okay. |

*She nods. They make their secret sign.*

| | |
|---|---|
| | What's a pact? |
| **REBECCA** | It's like a promise. Do you promise (*thinking*) to look after this island (*pause*) to keep it safe (*pause*) as long as you live? |

**Tony** *nods.*

| | |
|---|---|
| **REBECCA** | Say it. Say *I do*. |
| **TONY** | I do. I'll try. |
| **REBECCA** | Me, too. |

**Tony** *looks at his hands.* **Rebecca** *brings a small bowl of water and he washes them, and then smiles.*

| | |
|---|---|
| **TONY** | Look! Look! A boat. There's a boat! |
| **REBECCA** | Where? |
| **TONY** | I'm sure I saw it – out there, there it is again. |

| REBECCA | (*seeing it*) I see it. Dad, Dad! |
| TONY | Mum, Mum. There's a boat! |
| REBECCA | There's a boat on the horizon. |

**Martha** *and* **Gerald** *run in.* **Tony** *climbs the tree.*

| MARTHA | Is it coming here? Is it getting larger? |
| TONY | Yes, yes! |
| REBECCA | Can you see any people? |
| TONY | Not yet. |
| GERALD | What kind of boat? |
| TONY | I don't know. |
| MARTHA | I can see it. |
| TONY | Hey, over here! |
| REBECCA MARTHA | } (*together*) Hey, over here! |
| GERALD | Stop that – all of you. Stop it. |

*Silence.*

| | Tony, get down from the tree. Get down! |
| TONY | Why? |
| GERALD | We've got to think. Get down! |
| MARTHA | Think about what? |
| GERALD | We've got to scare them away. They can find their own island. This one's ours. |
| MARTHA | Gerald, we must help these people land. They'll be tired, like we were. They may be sick. |
| GERALD | You're right, they could be sick, carry disease. |
| TONY | Hey, over here! |
| GERALD | Tony, Tony! |

*He tries to pull* **Tony** *down.* **Rebecca** *tries to pull* **Gerald** *away.*

| REBECCA | Leave him alone. Leave him alone. |
| GERALD | Rebecca. This island is special, different. Are we going to let strangers spoil it? Are we? It's ours. |
| TONY | Hey! |
| GERALD | I won't tell you again. Get down! |
| TONY | No! I don't want it to be just us here. I want friends like I had before. Hey! |

| | |
|---|---|
| **GERALD** | Will you tell that boy to get down. |
| **MARTHA** | No. |
| **REBECCA** | How many people are there? |
| **TONY** | Six or seven. (*suddenly overjoyed*) And there are children. Children. There's children. |
| **REBECCA** | They'll need food and water. (*to* **Martha**) Don't just stand there. |
| **TONY** | (*leaping down from the tree*) I'll help! I'll help! |

*They begin to prepare bowls of food and drink which they carry to the front of the stage as a sign of welcome.*

| | |
|---|---|
| **GERALD** | Stop it, all of you! Will you please stop that. They're not welcome. Do you hear? Martha! |

**Martha** *looks at him and continues.*

Rebecca!

**Rebecca** *looks at him and continues.*

| | |
|---|---|
| | Tony, Tony! Stop it! Stop it! |
| **TONY** | You're hurting my arm. |
| **MARTHA** | Let him go, Gerald. |
| **TONY** | Let go! Let go! |

**Gerald** *smacks* **Tony** *around the face once.* **Tony** *cries out more in shock than pain.*

| | |
|---|---|
| **MARTHA** | How could you do that? |

**Martha** *comforts* **Tony.** **Gerald** *retreats and sits, head in hands.*

| | |
|---|---|
| **REBECCA** | (*pointing to the approaching boat*) Because he's scared, of them. |
| **GERALD** | I'm sorry, I'm sorry, I'm sorry. I just wanted it to be us. Just us. |
| **MARTHA** | Well it can't be *just us*. |

*Pause.*

Does it still hurt?

**Tony** *nods.*

| | |
|---|---|
| **REBECCA** | They're coming. (*waving*) Hello! |
| **MARTHA** | We've got to hurry, Tony. We've got friends. |

**Rebecca** *picks up her bowl and stands at the front of the stage.* **Martha** *and* **Tony** *join her.*

| | |
|---|---|
| **REBECCA** | I wonder what they'll be like. Will they speak our language? |
| **TONY** | There are three children. See? |
| **MARTHA** | Yes, yes. You can show them the island. |
| **TONY** | The mountains first. |
| **REBECCA** | Higher than high. |
| **TONY** | Cleaner than clean. |
| **REBECCA** | Whiter than white. |
| **MARTHA** | Then the lake. |
| **TONY** | Wider than wide. |
| **REBECCA** | Wetter than wet. |
| **TONY** | Then the forest. |
| **REBECCA** | Greener than green. |
| **TONY** | Deeper than deep. |

**Tony** *raises his bowl in symbolic greeting. The others follow.* **Gerald** *then stands and walks to their side. He lifts up the bowl.*

## END

# STARTING WORK ON THE PLAY

The playwright, Charles Way, took the story of Noah and the Ark as his starting point for the play. Noah was a good man living in violent times. God decided to punish people with a terrible flood, but Noah and his family and creatures from the animal world would be saved. He told Noah to build a huge ark as protection against the flood. According to the story, the flood lasted for about a year, and when at last the waters came down to a normal level, the ark came to rest among the mountains of Ararat in eastern Turkey.

Charles Way has made some fundamental changes to Noah's story: 'The first thing I did was remove God from the myth, and instead of a man, i.e. Noah, being the key survivor, I chose a woman, Mrs Noah, if you like. It is in these two changes that an enquiry into the play might start.

There are many reasons for the world being in a state of 'imbalance' – particularly in the environmental sphere – but it is my argument that one of the underlying reasons is the imbalance between the male and female sexes, an imbalance which has persisted through history so that many of our decisions and ways of behaving and believing, are not in keeping with the needs of the planet on which we live.

Traditionally, people have looked to religion, to gods, to help them choose how to relate to each other and to the environment. If we no longer believe in a god, however, how do we find a new morality to help and guide us? The children in the play put stones in a circle and make promises, an innocent but profound stab at a new culture, a religion that will protect the planet and the people in it.'

A good way of starting work on *The Flood* is to brainstorm your first responses as soon as you have read it. For this you will need some large sheets of paper and different coloured felt pens.

Working in small groups, write down words which describe your overall reactions to the play. Then look at the scenes in more detail.
● Which moments did you think had special impact?
● What sort of thoughts and feelings did you have at these key points in the play?

Now taking each character in turn, list words that describe personality, behaviour and how you think he or she may look. Then look at relationships between the characters. A diagram may help to describe the structure of character relationships. Then look at changes that take place in the play – particularly the changes in characters' attitudes and relationships. What causes these changes? Stick the first reactions charts on a wall, stand back and look at them. Now ask yourselves whether the play is just an interesting story, or whether it is trying to say something. Is it raising any issues or questions? Does the play have a message? Add your answers to the charts.

When directing a play or acting in it, you need to be clear about what the play is trying to say. Although this will become clearer during the rehearsals, your first reactions are important. They are less likely to be shaped by preconceived ideas which can affect the way you think and feel about the play. During rehearsals it is easy to lose a sense of its first impact. Remember that for an audience watching a performance it is the first reaction that matters. Keep your first reactions charts so that you can refer back to them during rehearsals.

Refer back to the points raised by Charles Way. How do the two key points fit into your first reactions chart?

## The balance of the sexes
Consider Martha's relationship to Gerald, before and during the play. Who makes the decisions? How do the children relate to each of their parents and to each other? What sort of changes in these relationships take place during the play? Why do the changes occur?

## The question of God
If we no longer believe in a god, we still have values and beliefs – less spiritual gods perhaps. What sort of gods does Gerald believe in? The flood strips away everything he thinks is valuable. He has to confront his fears about the world and learn to trust other people. We may think Gerald foolish, but how in a world where rapid changes take place can we know what are true values and what is ultimately good for people and the world in which we live?

Add any further thoughts that come up in discussion to the charts.

All these questions and points are not just to do with what the play is saying, but also to do with how, in a production, you may want to say it – the style of acting and staging. Although the play is about what happens to four characters during a great flood, its themes are universal. Martha, Gerald, Tony and Rebecca, while they are a particular family of two parents and two children, they also *represent* the family in society. This is a play in which characters, place, objects and events are important as *symbols*. (*The Flood* has been translated into Russian and produced by The Theatre for the Young Spectator at Rostov-on-Don, which indicates that the play can speak just as powerfully to people with a different language and culture. It may well be that in Russia at the present time where social and political changes are sweeping the country rather like a flood, the play has a special relevance for its audience.)

The emphasis in production should be less on a naturalistic portrayal of character and event, as in a television drama, and more on an economical style of staging in which every element is carefully chosen for its symbolic effect.

# STAGING THE PLAY

The dramatic interest in the play is not so much the flood disaster, as what the flood does to the four characters, how it affects what they do and, more importantly, how they think and feel. So when producing the play, you do not need to worry about how to create the effect of a real flood, a real house or island. The audience needs to see and know only what is relevant to the point of the play. Your production should eliminate all unnecessary detail and use only *essential* props and settings.

## SYMBOLS

It is important to remember that *everything* you do on stage affects the drama in some way. If you place a chair in the acting space, the audience will tend to give it special meaning. It will symbolise something. What the chair symbolises will depend on the type of chair. As a preparatory exercise compare these two appearances of a chair on stage:

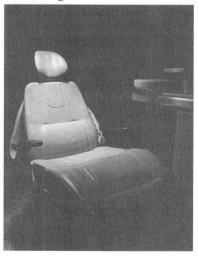

**Lighting – slow fade up of warm red glow**

**Lighting – single bright white spot switched on suddenly**

What information and impressions might the appearance of each chair give you?

Each chair is like a sign (or group of signs). It tells us something we need to know. Signs are a vitally important part of our everyday life. Some are so familiar that we take them for granted.

53

The signs above are simple. The chairs on stage are more complicated.
As well as giving us factual information, they symbolise feelings and
experiences. Symbols are like complex signs. They can represent aspects
of life that might take a long time to explain in words – beliefs, moods,
and concepts such as good and evil. So, for example, the rocking chair, as
well as being something for an actor to sit on, may also convey a mood of
homeliness, security, warmth and love. But we have to be careful not to
assume too much because people are different and what they see in a
symbol, will vary from person to person.

In *The Flood*, each element of staging – objects, sounds, lights – will be
important not just for what it is, but for what it *represents*.

## OBJECTS

In the play Gerald's briefcase is more than a bag to carry his papers and
plans. It symbolises many other aspects of his life.

1   In groups of three write a list of all the things you think Gerald's
briefcase represents.

2   The briefcase appears in Martha's dream, as do a toy clown and a pair
of dancing shoes. What do you think these objects symbolise?

3   Now take the idea of objects and symbols a step further. Assume you
have an empty performance space in which you are going to create
the house of Gerald and Martha – but with objects only.

(a)  Make a list of all the objects in the house mentioned in the play:
● table
● chairs
● breakfast cereals
● radio, etc.

(b)  Make notes on the type of house you think it is. Gerald is an up
and coming businessman – a yuppie, perhaps. The children have
plenty of toys. Add any other objects to your list that you think may
be helpful.

(c)  Now think how the look of each object may express the essence of
the family's life style.

Consider the table and chairs. Not any old table and chairs will do. They need to represent the sort of family they are. Are they ornate, upholstered, or of simple design all in white? In the first scene Gerald is getting dressed. What sort of clothes is he wearing for this special day at work? Think about the breakfast cereals. The presence of so many varieties on the table, (perhaps more than we would normally expect), as well as being visually impressive can also express the domestic life style that goes with Gerald's career aspirations.

Choose only those objects you think are needed. Make sure, as far as possible, that each one communicates what you want it to.

You will find it helpful to make notes and drawings before you set out to collect objects for your production.

# SOUND

## Music

Symbols speak directly to our feelings. They do not have to be explained in words. Music symbolises moods and feelings through sound.

Working again in small groups, take it in turns to talk about a piece of music that has a strong effect on you. It may make you feel happy or sad, or it may remind you of a particular experience.

In drama, music helps to build pictures in the audience's imagination. When the family find themselves on the shore of the island, a 'soft, strange music' is heard. We hear the music again later as they explore their island paradise. What sort of mood, feeling and picture should the music create? Talk about this in small groups.

Take care in your selection of music. Try different pieces, and listen to them with closed eyes. Some good music may remind us too much of other experiences to be of any use (e.g. music from TV adverts). You may have more success creating your own music. Synthesisers are useful for making continuous background sounds and for mixing melodies with harmony. You can also control the volumes easily during the performance, but be careful not to overdo the electronic sound. It may be that music played on a single instrument such as a flute is more effective than either recorder or synthesised sound. If so, take time to experiment by placing the instrument in different positions in relation to the acting area. Played in a room next door to the acting area, the flute may have a distant, magical sound which works perfectly.

## Sound effects

Sound effects in *The Flood* have a presence rather like that of a character. They are heard throughout the play – rain, flood tide, water lapping, strong wind, etc. and they affect the action on the stage. If you try recorded sound effects, listen to them carefully. You will find that they often do not provide the symbolic effect you want. A recording of a flood tide may sound to the audience simply like a sound effect of a flood tide and so fail to create the image that you want. You will need scratch free recordings (on CD, if possible), and a good sound system and speakers.

Remember that the dramatic effect of the rain, flood, waves, etc. takes place in the audience's imagination. Your aim should be to use sounds which trigger the imagination. With this you may have more success through creating live sounds – a tapping on a xylophone when the rain starts to 'pitter patter', a rolling on drums to represent storm clouds, and an orchestrated percussion sequence for the effect of a tidal wave. (This could have a stunning effect if you can assemble some large drums and place them around the outside of the audience so they are enveloped by a tidal wave of sound.)

The sequence of sounds in the play has clear sections like movements in a piece of music. Each movement has its own mood and *rhythm*. You can use the sounds as a sort of musical score which will give a structure to the performance of the play:

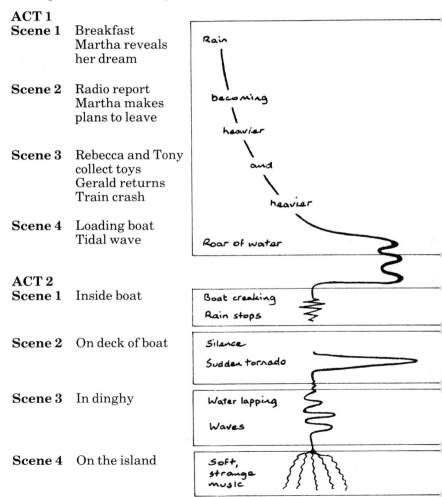

**ACT 1**
**Scene 1**  Breakfast
Martha reveals
her dream

**Scene 2**  Radio report
Martha makes
plans to leave

**Scene 3**  Rebecca and Tony
collect toys
Gerald returns
Train crash

**Scene 4**  Loading boat
Tidal wave

**ACT 2**
**Scene 1**  Inside boat

**Scene 2**  On deck of boat

**Scene 3**  In dinghy

**Scene 4**  On the island

56

# LIGHTING

As with music, light and colour symbolise mood and feeling. The scenes in *The Flood* have strong moods and atmospheres and these change as the play progresses. When planning your production, think carefully about how you can use light to convey the shifts of mood. If you have only a few stage lanterns in school, it will be worth borrowing or hiring some extras and a portable dimming unit.

## Colour

We often associate certain colours with particular moods; for example, yellow with brightness and happiness, and dark blue and grey with sad and sombre moods. When thinking about lighting the play, choose your colours carefully. You can get sample sets of colour gels for lanterns from a theatrical supplier. These will help you to decide before you buy (and possibly save on expense). Mood and atmosphere change throughout the play and colour contrasts will heighten the changes:

Shaft of sunlight ........... General stage light: dark grey, steel blue – low
through the clouds         level. Sunlight: two narrow spots, almost
(Act 2 Scene 2)            overhead, one white, the other light yellow,
                           slightly larger than the white to create a halo
                           effect.

The island .................... The first real colour in the play – green, blue,
                           yellow for woods and lakes; bright white light
                           with some straw gels for the open air and beach.

## Light patterns

With certain types of stage lantern, e.g. a Strand patt 23, you can create patterned light effects by slotting in a sheet metal 'slide' called a *gobo*. A gobo has a pattern cut into it which shapes the light from the lantern. The light and the pattern can be focussed like a projector. Here are some that may be useful in *The Flood*. If you cannot obtain these from a local theatrical supplier, you can buy them directly from DHA Lighting Ltd., 3, Jonathan Street, London SE11 5NH.

Water 1

Water 4

Cross-fading two gobos can give the effect of moving water. Alternatively, you could hire a water ripple effect. This is simple to use, but you may find the patterned gobos more effective.

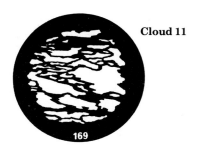

Cloud 11

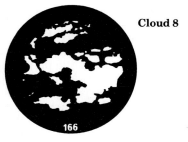

Cloud 8

These cloud images may work better slightly out of focus. For the island, you could create exciting mottled effects of sun through trees.

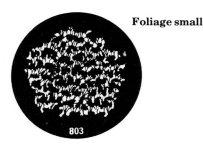

Foliage small

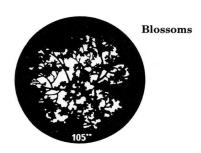

Blossoms

If you have enough lanterns, you could create various patterns to represent different areas of the island.

## ACTING SPACE

Setting the play will not be complicated. You will simply need an open area with easy access on and off stage. The locations of scenes – house, boat, dinghy, island – can be established by objects which change with the scenes. The backcloth may be more of a problem. To get the best out of the lighting and the changes of mood and atmosphere in the play, you will need a large light reflective area. If you do not have a backcloth, a blank wall (with a new coat of white paint) may work just as well. Another way of heightening the effect of the lighting is to cover the acting area with a floor cloth (stretched and stuck down with tape). This works as a sort of projection screen making light patterns and colours strong and exciting. By shining light onto a floor cloth you immediately transform the space and create a theatrical atmosphere, especially if you use patterned gobos, e.g. mottled sunlight on the island or waves on the sea. It will be expensive to buy a floor cloth but you may be able to borrow one from a local theatre company.

*The Flood* could work well in a variety of stage/audience arrangements:

1 **Proscenium arch stage** with backcloth or white wall. Chorus and musical instruments placed on either side of the stage, in front of the arch.

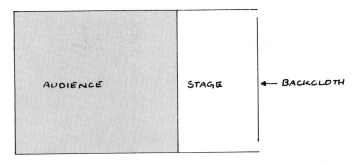

2 **'In the round'**, i.e. with the audience on all sides. No backcloth. The chorus occupying one block of seats or surrounding the action using either the front or back row. The musical instruments placed behind so the audience feel they are in the centre of the sound.

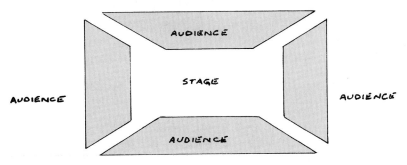

3 **Thrust stage** with the audience on three sides. Backcloth or wall. Chorus and instruments – similar to an 'in the round' layout.

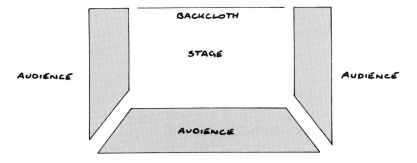

Make basic decisions about the layout early in the production process to give plenty of time for experiment with lights and sound.

# MARTHA'S DREAM

A good starting point for technical experiment is Martha's dream. All the points about the symbolic effect of objects, sound and light apply to the staging of this first scene of the play.

The dream should be beautiful and yet disturbing. Though only a short sequence, it requires careful crafting – colours should blend, movements flow, light and sound changes be co-ordinated. Technically, it presents a few difficulties. One of these is the silhouette. If you do not have a backcloth, or if you cannot make enough space for the silhouette cut-out, the city landscape could be projected on to the back wall using gobos:

 City lights

 Nightlights 3

In this way you can operate the disappearance and return of the city on the dimmer control.

Other problems may be the lifting of the objects – briefcase, toy clown and shoes, and the black and white birds. Rather than use strings over lighting bars, which will be difficult to control, you could use a team of stage hands dressed in black and merging in and out of the shadows to manipulate the objects. Though the operators will be seen by the audience they will seem like shadowy figures in Martha's dream (but only if their movements are carefully planned).

Do not rush the dream. Build mood and atmosphere step by step:

1 Darkness (hold for 10 seconds).
2 Slow fade up city lights (hold for 20 seconds to give the audience time to take in the image).
3 Sound of rain – very faint.
4 Over 30 seconds build sound to a downpour, almost menacing in its itensity.
5 Slow fade up of central overhead spot on Martha in the boat, creating a strong image of her isolation in a great expanse of water.

Now you continue this step by step build-up of mood and atmosphere.

When experimenting like this, you are working like a sculptor, but using light, sound, space, etc. as your materials. Keep an observer's eye on what you work. Is it the effect you want? How can it be improved? To create a smooth dream-like effect you will need plenty of practice. Any uncertainty in performance and the magical atmosphere will be lost.

# CREATING THE CHARACTERS

The play has four main characters – Martha, Gerald, Rebecca and Tony – and a Chorus. When casting the play, you could, if you wish, divide up the main parts by having a set of four characters for each main section of the play – home, boat and island. Changing over from one set to another could be done easily between scenes. The Chorus should have as many voices as possible, so try to arrange for the main actors to join the Chorus when not performing in the play. Ideas on how to develop the Chorus can be found on pp. 74–75. The four family characters are all very different from each other and they require some careful study in order to portray them in performance.

Try reading through the play in groups of four or five. Each group should be responsible for finding out about one character only from things that they say or do, and jotting down their findings in list form. Here is an example:

**Martha**
- thinks deeply about things
- is ready to argue for her own point of view
- is determined and brave
- does not believe all she reads in the papers or sees on the television.

You should make a note of the exact line or action in the play from which you have gained your evidence.

You might record your findings in the manner of a gingerbread figure such as the one opposite, writing what you find out about the character inside the figure. You might choose to write what the character says inside the figure and what other characters say about, or to them, in the space outside.

You could make a group statue or still image about your character. It might involve one of your group as the 'statue' and the others as collaborative sculptors who will mould the statue as with a 'bendy toy' into a position which represents his/her characteristics.

Or, you might choose to involve your whole group in the sculpture, perhaps to represent the character in a more abstract form. It is possible to show a number of sides to a person's character in this manner.

Now give your sculpture a title. Discuss this with the rest of your class when they have seen your sculpture, and listen to their alternatives.

Write the alternatives down around the base of the statue. You might wish to change your statue, however slightly, as a result of discussing these impressions.

Choose one member of your group to be interviewed by the others. They must answer the questions as if they are your group's chosen character. You might have a special chair for this person to sit on during the interview. You may wish the person being interviewed to adopt a suitable style of speech and vocabulary for the character they are answering for. You may also wish them to experiment with physical mannerisms. It is useful if you decide on an actual point in relation to the interview chair where the 'acting space' begins. Your group member is clear then about when they need to 'become' the character and when they change back to themselves. A circle of light can be useful for this. If lighting is not available an area marked with string, chalk or P.E. mats works very well.

All characters have a background and a personal history. We only learn a little about their lives from the glimpse that we are given of them in a play script. It is useful, when acting a character to have some idea of the life that they might have led before the play began, which has helped to shape their ideas and values.

As you get used to the interviewing exercise, you could change the member of your group being interviewed, or use all your group to represent your character, perhaps taking turns to answer, and be questioned by the rest of the class. The questioners might prepare for the interview by drawing up a chart as follows:

| WHAT DO WE KNOW ABOUT...? | WHAT DO WE THINK WE KNOW ABOUT...? | WHAT WOULD WE LIKE TO KNOW ABOUT...? |
|---|---|---|
| 1 | 1 | 1 |
| 2 | 2 | 2 |
| 3 | 3 | 3 |

The person being interviewed should make up background as they are questioned, and these answers should be noted and later discussed.

Now go back and remake your statue with alterations based on the information you have discovered and invented.

The physical mannerisms of a character can be hard to decide upon. They should help the audience to understand what the character is like as a personality. It is easy to think that you only have to make the actions suit the words or situation. All people have habitual ways of standing, moving, sitting and using their hands, etc. It is helpful to an actor to decide some basic movements of this sort for the character that they are portraying.

Try making two sets of cards. On one set write down various different parts of the body, such as hands, feet, knees, etc. Write one part on each card. On the other set write down simple human characteristics, such as shy, angry, inquisitive, etc. Again, write one word on each card. The cards are then placed, in their separate piles, somewhere in the rehearsal space. Members of the group then turn up a card for a characteristic, returning it to the bottom of the pile, and in the same manner they then turn up a body part. A scene may then be improvised using two or three actors in a group. The cards they turned up should be kept secret. A simple scene such as returning a faulty purchase to a shop would do. The actors might then be asked to guess what cards had been chosen and how suitable those cards had been to the purpose of the scene.

Various scenes from the play might then be tried by giving each character one or two body part cards and one or two characteristics, either as a result of discussion or by chance. The results can be discussed and developed until suitable mannerisms are found.

A simple exercise once the mannerisms are beginning to form is to try the character out doing different simple everyday things. These might include:

- making a cup of tea
- entering and leaving a room
- sitting down in a familiar chair
- buying a train ticket.

The rest of the class or group could watch these activities and share their comments on the results.

Try taking characters out of the play and putting them in suitable situations outside the events that we see in the play. Here are some examples of possible situations:

- Gerald being interviewed for a job
- Martha buying the boat
- Tony describing his goldfish to his teacher
- Rebecca explaining her mother's dreams to a friend.

Create a series of still images or statues to explain how your character has become the person he/she is today. The final picture will be the one that you have already created. You might make four or five that come before it in the series.

In groups of two or four, choose a scene from the play and read it through three times. Decide what character you are going to be and read it through once more aloud. Put the script away and try to go through the scene in your own words, concentrating on how your character behaves and what he or she is trying to achieve in the scene. It is very difficult to portray a character with a book in your hands, so this kind of work is very important until you have learned the words.

If you decide to involve more than just four of your group or class in the performance of the main characters, you will also need to devise as a whole group the chief physical mannerisms of each character, and to keep them simple.

Practise passing the characters from one person to another, rather like a game of tag. Sit in a circle and get four actors to begin a scene from the play. They act it out in the centre of the circle. At any time, an actor can 'tag' one of the audience who will take over straightaway. The idea is for the new performer to adopt, as closely as possible, the agreed mannerism(s) of the character.

This exercise can be particularly helpful when the list of actors who will play any one character has been finalised.

The swopping of actors during a performance may still be confusing to an audience even if mannerisms are copied and agreed carefully. Try the following to make things more clear:

All the actors who are to play one character should go through the play and note down which pieces of costume the character *must* have. Many of these are mentioned in the script, such as:

. . . *Rebecca brings him his* **coat** *and* **hat**. (page 7)

These items may be easily obtained by the actors from home, but make sure that anything that is used fits *all* the actors easily.

Try reading through your list and deciding on one item of costume that, perhaps with a little 'cheating', your character could wear all the time. For example:

| | |
|---|---|
| TONY | A baseball-type cap |
| GERALD | A jacket (rather than whole suit) |
| REBECCA | A sweatshirt |
| MARTHA | A cardigan |

It is important that these things can be taken off and put on quickly.

The actors of the main parts, when they are not required for their scene, can take their place amongst the Chorus.

It is not necessary for the change of actors to take place in secret. You might try an arrangement such as this:

● Place four stands (similar to old-fashioned hall hat stands), at the corners, or edges, of your acting area, close to the entrances and exits, but in full view of the audience. The real thing can be quite expensive but a home-made version is just as good.

● Write the name of each character on a board and fix one board to the top of each stand. All items of that character's costume can be kept on their own stand. When an actor finishes her scene, she removes her costume items and hangs them on the stand. Another actor takes over by removing items from the stand and putting them on. It is important that this process appears slick rather than rushed, so spend time during rehearsal practising the changeover.

● Other than the essential items of costume you have decided upon, *all* the actors in your performance should wear basic clothing of similar colour. This colour should preferably be dark, such as blue or black. Bring in things from home and share or swop them around in your group until the whole class takes on a similar appearance. It is important that these clothes are not too large so that Gerald's jacket, for example, fits over them easily.

This is one method of using the costume stands. You might discover your own.

Costumes can, of course, be tidily kept on the stands between performances. It makes checking that everything is there before you start much easier too!

Do not forget that promotional T-shirts with the name of the play written on the front or back are easily obtained. The whole group could wear these for performances.

# TENSIONS AND TURNING POINTS

Working with a script can present practical difficulties that you do not find when building plays through improvisation. These are some of them:

- Actors keep their eyes on the book, waiting for their turn to speak and ignoring what is going on around them.
- Lines are spoken with a repetitive rhythm and tone, and with no sense of their *purpose* within the scene.
- Words seem more important than actions, making it difficult to imagine what characters *do* on stage and how they communicate through gesture, mannerism, etc.

If you cannot overcome these problems, the scenes fail to come to life. All sorts of elements contribute to the power of a play to grip our imaginations, but the most important element is *dramatic tension*. Lighting, sound effects, setting and costumes play a vital part, but they are not the drama. Their purpose is to heighten the dramatic tensions arising from the interaction of characters within the situation.

Like a good story, dramatic tensions demand our attention. We sense them very quickly when watching a play, and they give us a 'What's going to happen next?' feeling. Dramatic tensions cause things to happen in a play. They cannot be sustained for ever and at some point they have to break – feelings boil over, a character does something unexpected, somebody breaks down in tears, takes command, admits to something he or she has been denying all along, or simply falls about laughing. These moments in a play may not resolve tension, they may shift it or even increase it. Whatever follows them, they feel like *turning points* in the drama. They bring about change in the way characters think or what they do, or in the way the audience responds. Drama is essentially about the tensions and changes that take place in the lives of the characters. Some changes are small, for example, a daughter being persuaded by her mother after an argument to wear a dress she does not like for a family party; but others may be much more significant, for example, the collapse of a person's long held spiritual beliefs, or an event such as the unintentional killing of a loved one.

Tensions and turning points are what makes drama dramatic. They give the play and the scenes within it their purpose. If you know the tensions and turning points of scenes in rehearsal, then you know what you are working towards and what you are trying to communicate to the audience. They help you to work out how the characters behave, how to place them on stage and to use pauses and actions to convey what characters are thinking *but not saying.*

If tensions are to work, the characters must be believable. If the audience cannot identify with the characters, they will not feel any tension in the play. So developing belief in the characters is very important and you should bear in mind the advice given on pages 61–66 when following these suggestions for rehearsing the play.

Here are two examples of how to develop scenes in rehearsal, by working through their dramatic tensions and turning points.

## Act 1 Scene 2

The scene following Martha's dream. It is breakfast time and Gerald is getting ready for work, excited by the prospects of his future career. Martha is still in a dream-like state, trying to understand what the dream is telling her.

As preparation for working on the scene actively, first divide into groups of five and do the following:

● Read through the scene.

● Talk about the dramatic impact of the scene, and decide which parts have the strongest tensions.

● Take a long piece of paper and draw a graph to represent visually the flow of dramatic tension and the turning points in the scene.

In this scene you could say that there are two turning points where dramatic tension is heightened:

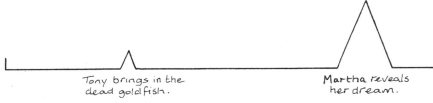

Tony brings in the dead goldfish.

Martha reveals her dream.

1   Tony's appearance with the goldfish is like an omen of worse things to come, but we are not sure what. This is not a normal day; things are going wrong, the routine is threatened.

2   The main turning point in the scene is when we know at last what the dream means. There will be a great flood. (This is the first time we hear the word 'flood'.) We must believe Martha – disaster is certain. How will the family react? What will the flood do to them?

Here is the basic principle about how drama works. Dramatic tension does not run on one level throughout the play, but it has high and low points. The low points are vitally important in building towards the moments of high tension which cause turning points in the action.

The whole scene builds to Martha's revelation of the meaning of her dream. From the beginning, Martha has been trying to communicate her dream to Gerald, but he dismisses her and advises psychiatric help. When working on the scene, think carefully about the balance of attitudes between Martha and Gerald, and avoid extreme terpretations. If Martha looks deranged and pathetic, or Gerald an ter fool, they will be less believable and the tension will be weakened. he scene could then easily become a monotonous verbal argument tween the two. Martha should convey a deep inner conviction that the eam is telling her the truth, and Gerald should respond as we might pect most people to do in such a circumstance: he rejects the threat to e familiar world and persists with the normal routine.

Now let us take a close director's view of the second half of the scene to e how tension can build to the main turning point – Martha explaining r dream.

Think first about the layout of the scene in the acting space. emember the design should be as simple as possible to focus the idience's attention on the characters and the situation.

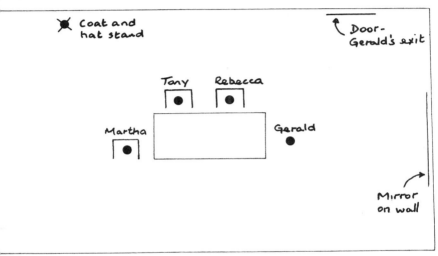

ony appears with the dead goldfish, and Rebecca makes fun of him:

| | |
|---|---|
| ₤BECCA | Feed it to next door's cat. |
| ₤NY | Mum. |
| ₤BECCA | Brown Owl says we should recycle all our waste. |
| ₤NY | He's not waste. He's my fish. |
| ₤BECCA | Was. |

becca *makes a fish face at* Tony *and he loses control. He chases her,* *outing as he does so.*

| | |
|---|---|
| ₤RALD | Ha! |
| ₤RTHA | Children. Tony, stop that! Rebecca. |
| ₤RALD | Perhaps you should see someone. |
| ₤RTHA | What? |

*e children fall suddenly silent.*

| | |
|---|---|
| ₤RALD | I said (*pause*) . . . perhaps you should see someone. |
| ₤RTHA | Who? |
| ₤RALD | I don't know – a psychiatrist. |

*Martha still in her dream (facing front), not yet fully realising what the dream means.*
*Normally she is able to cope with the children's behaviour at breakfast, but not today.*

*Gerald is looking at himself in the mirror – ('Is the tie straight?') – trying to control himself.*

69

| TONY | What's that? |
|------|------|
| MARTHA | I don't need a psychiatrist. I need you. |
| TONY | What's going on? |
| MARTHA | I need to talk – now. |
| GERALD | Not in front of them. |
| TONY | Why? |
| GERALD | Your mother isn't very well. |
| TONY | Is that true? Is it? |
| MARTHA | I . . . (shrugging) I have this dream . . . |
| GERALD | Martha! I'll get you another goldfish. |
| REBECCA | Boring. |
| MARTHA | Don't be cruel. |
| REBECCA | Why not? (pause) |
| TONY | Has my fish gone to Heaven? |
| REBECCA | Heaven doesn't exist, does it, Dad? There's only the here and now. The rest is all make-believe like Father Christmas. |
| TONY | Is that true? |
| MARTHA | There are things that your father and sister and even Brown Owl do not understand. There are other worlds besides this one. Your fish is at peace. Peace is another world, another place where people are not cruel. |
| TONY | Is Arthur there? |
| MARTHA | I hope so. |
| GERALD | The fish is dead – that's all. I'll get you one that works. I must go. |
| MARTHA | Gerald . . . Gerald you can't go – not today. |
| GERALD | Rebecca. |

As is their routine, **Rebecca** brings him his coat and hat.

| MARTHA | Please, (dropping to her knees) I . . . I beg you. |

Silence. They all stare at **Martha**.

| TONY | Mum? |

**Rebecca** then brings a briefcase to her father but **Martha** grabs it.

| GERALD | Martha. |
|------|------|
| MARTHA | In the dream I had last night, something new happened. |
| GERALD | Give me the briefcase. |
| MARTHA | No. |
| GERALD | Are you crazy? |
| MARTHA | If you won't talk to me, then just listen. |
| GERALD | Give me my briefcase. Give it me. (They struggle for it.) Give it. |

*Handwritten margin annotations:*

The children know the sugges[tion] is a serious one – ('Is Mummy going mad?').

Tony and Rebecca watch M[artha]. Tony knows something is the matter.

Now putting on her shoes. To Tony, while tying the laces.

Rebecca returns to her cereal. Like her father she sticks to the morning routi[ne].

Crunches cereal in he[r] mouth.

Martha sits up, still i[n] her dream, but at las[t] beginning to realise what it means.

Gerald now fully dress[ed] and checking his overal[l] appearance in the mirr[or] still in control – just.

Rebecca walks to the co[at] stand and then to Ger[ald] in front of Martha as though to make a poin[t].

A change in Martha. For the first time she turns and looks at Gera[ld] directly. Speaks with inner certainty.

Hold this silence. Audience must have tim[e] to wonder about Martha['s] inner turmoil which is now becoming more visible. Gerald is the la[st] to look at Martha.

Clutches the briefcase to her, rocking slightly on her knees.

Gerald loses self control. The struggle is sordid and physical and quite prolonged. Martha hangs on to the briefcase desperately.

70

| REBECCA | Stop fighting! You're always fighting. |
| --- | --- |

Martha *pulls away with the case.*

| GERALD | The most important day . . . |
| --- | --- |
| MARTHA | Something new happened. My dream took place at sea. |

*Silence.*

| GERALD | All right, you have the case. You talk. Then I'll have the case and I'll go to work. |
| --- | --- |
| MARTHA | How long has it been raining? |
| TONY | Three days. |
| MARTHA | And three nights of solid rain. |
| GERALD | You want to talk about the weather? |
| MARTHA | It's not going to stop raining. The dream, you see. It's not going to stop raining until everything is destroyed, swept away. (*She grabs the newspaper.*) Look, look! It's started, accidents caused by floods, and, and it isn't going to stop until the whole world is beneath water, the buildings, the animals, the people. You have to stay here and think of a way of escaping, surviving the flood. |

*Silence.*

| TONY | Is that true? |
| --- | --- |
| GERALD | No Tony, that isn't true. Martha you're not well. I didn't realise how . . . but we'll sort it out. |
| REBECCA | Dad? |
| GERALD | Don't worry. Your mother is just teasing. A game. The world is not going to end. I mean, what would be the point of me going to work if the world was going to end – which it isn't – it's never ending. |

*He takes* **Martha** *to one side.*

We'll talk later, tonight, in depth, for as long as you want. I promise, I promise.

*Rebecca gives him his umbrella.*

| GERALD | I don't think I'll be needing that. |
| --- | --- |
| TONY | Don't forget my goldfish. |

*Exit Gerald. A moment later he returns and picks up the umbrella, smiles and leaves.*

Gerald has lost his neat businessman's look. Tries to humour Martha, but only as a way of getting the case.

Spoken in the calm *after* the physical struggle – not in anger, but with the clarity and conviction of knowing the truth.

Hold the silence – the impact sinks in. Each character reacts differently – Tony on the edge of terror, Rebecca not sure what to think, looks to her father. Gerald thinking, 'As I thought, only a doctor can help'.

Gerald gives a patronising pat on Martha's shoulder. Tries a calm tone of voice, but we see through it – his real aim is to get the briefcase.

Still wanting to behave as if things were normal. Tries to collect his umbrella without losing face.

71

## Act 2 Scene 5

While each scene in *The Flood* has its own tensions and turning points, the play overall builds to one special turning point in the final moment of the last scene. Here the family learn that they are not the only survivors of the flood and they prepare to welcome the strangers to the island. By this point, every member of the family has been affected or changed by the flood, but whereas Martha, Tony and Rebecca have accepted the need to change, Gerald has resisted it. The challenge to him is, perhaps, more fundamental. He has to abandon the hopes, ambitions and values he has held dear for so long, and more than the others, he feels the need to cling on to what he knows, what makes him feel secure, his authority and power. But in the final moments of the play he is able to raise the bowl of food as a gesture of welcome. When the family faces the approaching strangers before raising the bowls, we have a fairly good idea about what Martha, Tony and Rebecca think, but we are still guessing about what Gerald will do. By now we know a lot about him, what matters to him and how he thinks and feels. But this is the ultimate test. How will he react? Will he retreat into his fear, or take the brave step and accept their arrival? His gesture of offering is charged with significance, but is it a genuine gesture of welcome or simply that he has no alternative?

If you rush the staging of this final scene its dramatic power will be lost. So plan it carefully. Start a couple of pages from the end of the play.

Tony is up a tree from which he can see the strangers arriving in their boat. Gerald is panicking:

| | |
|---|---|
| TONY | *(leaping down from the tree)* I'll help! I'll help! |

*They begin to prepare bowls of food and drink which they carry to the front of the stage as a sign of welcome.*

| | |
|---|---|
| GERALD | Stop it, all of you! Will you please stop that. They're not welcome. Do you hear? Martha! |

**Martha** *looks at him and continues.*

Rebecca!

**Rebecca** *looks at him and continues.*

Tony, Tony! Stop it! Stop it!

*The preparations are animated. The food itself looks inviting. Bowls are arranged with care, rather like a ritual. Gerald trapped in his own panic.*

*Gerald is isolated by his anger. Rebecca, his former ally, now more independent. She wants to get on with what she sees needs to be done.*

*Gerald seizes Tony, the weakest member of the family. Another sordid outbreak of violence. Gerald has reached the end of the line.*

72

| | |
|---|---|
| TONY | You're hurting my arm. |
| MARTHA | Let him go, Gerald. |
| TONY | Let go! Let go! |

**Gerald** *smacks* **Tony** *around the face once.* **Tony** *cries out more in shock than pain.*

| | |
|---|---|
| MARTHA | How could you do that? |

**Martha** *comforts* **Tony.** **Gerald** *retreats and sits, head in hands.*

| | |
|---|---|
| REBECCA | *(pointing to the approaching boat)* Because he's scared, of them. |
| GERALD | I'm sorry, I'm sorry, I'm sorry. I just wanted it to be us. Just us. |
| MARTHA | Well it can't be *just us.* |

*Pause.*

Does it still hurt?

**Tony** *nods.*

| | |
|---|---|
| REBECCA | They're coming. *(waving)* Hello! |
| MARTHA | We've got to hurry, Tony. We've got friends. |

**Rebecca** *picks up her bowl and stands at the front of the stage.* **Martha** *and* **Tony** *join her.*

| | |
|---|---|
| REBECCA | I wonder what they'll be like. Will they speak our language? |
| TONY | There are three children. See? |
| MARTHA | Yes, yes. You can show them the island. |
| TONY | The mountains first. |
| REBECCA | Higher than high. |
| TONY | Cleaner than clean. |
| REBECCA | Whiter than white. |
| MARTHA | Then the lake. |
| TONY | Wider than wide. |
| REBECCA | Wetter than wet. |
| TONY | Then the forest. |
| REBECCA | Greener than green. |
| TONY | Deeper than deep. |

**Tony** *raises his bowl in symbolic greeting. The others follow.* **Gerald** *then stands and walks to their side. He lifts up the bowl.*

*[Handwritten margin note:]* Each picks up bowl slowly. Pause as they each silently contemplate the strangers' arrival. Music – quiet, distant, harmonious. Lights narrow to a single spot (focussing more on what goes on inside their heads). Lines spoken with space for the music in between.

*[Handwritten note at bottom:]* Tony, the youngest, then Rebecca, then Martha, like a formal pattern which cannot be completed without Gerald. His bowl is ready. Gerald turns and watches them. Music. Stands and walks to them slowly. Looks at the bowl, not sure if he can join them – perhaps he is on the point of turning away – but then stops – turns again to the bowl, slowly picks it up and offers it forward (completing the pattern).

73

# THE CHORUS

It is easy to think that the Chorus will just stand at the back, or sit at the front of the acting area and wait for their turn to speak or sing. This does not have to be the case. Try the following:

1   In groups of four, two people read the script while the others experiment with suitable background sounds, such as the rain falling or the island jungle. They can only use the sounds that they can make with their hands and voices. These experiments could be tape-recorded for reference. Hand clapping, quietly and at varying rhythms makes very good rain effects. Let other groups hear these effects and select and practise those which seem to work the best.

   Repeat the above exercise but this time using instruments such as home-made percussion or recorders, in order to provide background or punctuation to the voices. It is most effective if simple sequences are repeated at intervals in the speech rather than played continuously.

2   In groups of six go through a choral speech, marking those parts which could be stressed, i.e:

   Pitter patter, pitter pat (page 1)

   You do not *all* have to say *all* the words. Try using two of your group to say most of the speech, only using the whole group for the parts that you have marked. Perform your piece to other groups and discuss their impressions.

   You do not have to speak all the words as you would do in real life. Certain words, either because of the way they sound or because of their importance, can be slurred, slowed down, increased in volume or sung. Take a short extract in small groups and experiment with the different ways that the extract can sound. Share your work with others as a performance.

3   Select extracts from the work you have done and try them out as a whole group. Remember to have those of you who are doing the same things sitting close together, like an orchestra, so that you can support each other.

4   In groups of six, create a simple moving image, just using your arms and upper body, that matches an extract of choral speech that you have chosen. Here are two suggestions:
   rising and falling        waves
   swaying                   island trees

5   You might try making some simple masks for the Chorus to wear. Animal and/or green coloured masks would be effective for the island

scenes. Remember not to cover the lower face with these masks or sound quality will be impaired.

6  In performance it is much better if members of the Chorus do not just file onto the stage or acting space, like a school crocodile. Try out different ways and times of entering:

●  Be there before the audience arrives.

●  Enter as the audience does. Remember that these 'casual' effects need careful practice to work well. You might try giving numbers to each Chorus member so they know when their turn comes.

●  Enter as a procession, in formal style, at the start of the first speech so that you are all in place by the dream. This could be particularly effective if combined with a gradual increase in lighting.

●  It is effective if whatever you decide upon for the opening of the play is repeated, in reverse, for the close; for example, staying on stage until the audience has gone, leaving in a formal procession, etc.

# PERFORMANCE PROJECT
## THE LIFE OF GERALD (AND HIS FAMILY)

> TODAY I TAKE OVER, I SIGN THE DEALS, I MAKE THE MONEY, WE'RE GOING TO BE RICH.

> PLANS, PLANS FOR NEW BUILDINGS, HOUSES, HOTELS... OFFICES. PLANS FOR THE FUTURE DEVELOPMENT OF THE WORLD.

> I'LL TAKE MY POWER BALL, AND MY SPACE GUN AND MY MASTERS OF THE UNIVERSE.

> I'LL TAKE MY CALCULATOR ... AND A RADIO, DANCING SHOES.

In the Bible story, God sent the flood because he was displeased with people. In the play, the flood is not a punishment from God but a natural disaster which washes away everything that makes life normal for Gerald and his family. When at last they find themselves on land, they must come to terms with a new and very different world and create for themselves a new sense of normality. What seemed so important in the old world has no value in the new. Gerald's plans are useful only for making paper aeroplanes.

What sort of things make life normal for us? The most important things we often take for granted – relationships, places, possessions, routines – make life predictable. Familiar things and patterns of behaviour hold within them what we believe to be important and valuable, though we may not be aware that this is so until something happens that threatens to change them.

Go back to the charts recording your first reactions to *The Flood*.

1 Highlight all the comments you made to do with the family's life style, values and attitudes *before* the flood threatened.

2 Look through the text for statements and actions by characters that indicate what makes life 'normal' for them.

3 In groups of three or four, create still pictures portraying specific aspects of the family's life style, values and attitudes. Some of these may not be from the play directly but depict closely related situations, such as Gerald at work and the children at school or with their friends. Give each picture a specific setting. Add the statements as captions.

4 As well as building still pictures, you could create very short scenes, each no longer than eight seconds, like a film clip. Each scene or clip should express something typical about the family or one of its members. (Remember that many of the things that make life seem normal, such as Pops, Crispies and Flakes for breakfast, they probably take for granted.)

5 Combine these pictures and clips to create a continuous performance which expresses the values and attitudes of the family. The performance will be very short, perhaps no longer than two minutes, but could be very effective if:

● each picture or clip conveys clearly its particular attitude or idea
● the words and action flow smoothly in a continous sequence.

One way of doing this is to create the performance with two linked groups. Each group first devises its own pictures and clips, then they work together to build a sequence by alternating pictures or clips between the two groups. In performance each group has its own space and lights and the sequence runs by *cross-fading* from one to the other.

6 You could use the same dramatic technique focusing on your own lives. Look at the things you do as a matter of routine, things you look forward to and things you are obliged to do. What possessions have significance? Like Gerald's briefcase and work, objects and routines can mean more than they seem to do. Rather than try to cover everything, you could perhaps concentrate on life at home and at school through a typical day. Some things you chose may seem insignificant but nevertheless they are a part of your day to day structure that helps to make life feel normal. Create pictures with captions, and 'film clips' as in the exercise above and link them together in a short performance. Performing the details of life that we take for granted can make us look at familiar things in a fresh way and, perhaps, question the values that they hold for us.

# PERFORMANCE PROJECT
## MR NOAH AND THE FLOOD

Ancient stories of a great flood are worldwide. An epic tale from Babylon tells of how the gods sent a flood because they could not stand the noise people were making on earth. In the Bible story, the whole world is under the control of one God. He sends the flood to punish people for the violent deeds being committed everywhere:

**6** 9–10 This is the story of Noah. He had three sons, Shem, Ham, and Japheth. Noah had no faults and was the only good man of his time. He lived in fellowship with God, [11]but everyone else was evil in God's sight, and violence had spread everywhere. [12] God looked at the world and saw that it was evil, for the people were all living evil lives.

13 God said to Noah, "I have decided to put an end to all mankind. I will destroy them completely, because the world is full of their violent deeds. [14]Build a boat for yourself out of good timber; make rooms in it and cover it with tar inside and out. [15]Make it 133 metres long, 22 metres wide, and 13 metres high. [16]Make a roof for the boat and leave a space of 44 centimetres between the roof and the sides. Build it with three decks and put a door in the side. [17]I am going to send a flood on the earth to destroy every living being. Everything on the earth will die, [18]but I will make a covenant with you. Go into the boat with your wife, your sons, and their wives. [19-20]Take into the boat with you a male and a female of every kind of animal and of every kind of bird, in order to keep them alive. [21]Take along all kinds of food for you and for them." [22]Noah did everything that God commanded.

**7** 11 When Noah was six hundred years old, on the seventeenth day of the second month all the outlets of the vast body of water beneath the earth burst open, all the floodgates of the sky were opened, [12]and rain fell on the earth for forty days and nights. [13]On the same day Noah and his wife went into the boat with their three sons, Shem, Ham, and Japheth, and their wives. [14]With them went every kind of animal, domestic and wild, large and small, and every kind of bird. [15]A male and a female of each kind of living being went into the boat with Noah, [16]as God had commanded. The the Lord shut the door behind Noah.

17 The flood continued for forty days and the water became deep enough the boat to float. [18]The water became deeper, and the boat drifted on the surface. [19]It became so deep that covered the highest mountains; [20]It went on rising until it was about seven metres above the tops of the mountains. [21]Every living being on the earth died every bird every animal and every person. [22]Everything on earth that breathed died. [23]The Lord destroyed all living beings on the earth – human beings, animals, and birds. The only ones left were Noah and those who were with him in the boat. [24]The water did not stop going down for a hundred and fifty

Many areas of Britain today suffer from a constant threat of flooding. From time to time a disaster occurs (though not on the same scale as in Noah's time).

At midday on Monday, 26 February 1990, violent storms breached the sea wall at Towyn, North Wales. For five days waves crashed through the gap flooding an area of ten square miles. Many people had to leave their homes with little more than the clothes they stood up in. Around 2,900 houses were damaged and more than 5,000 people had to be evacuated.

London opened the Thames Barrier in 1982 to prevent the city from flooding by a freak high tide, but the risk has not disappeared completely. Emergency planning is still necessary but so far this has not been properly co-ordinated. The east coast of Lincolnshire where the land rises little above sea level, depends on its sea defences for protection. Some areas are vulnerable even without a high tide. The East Lindsey District Council in Lincolnshire has prepared these notes as guidance to the general public in the event of a flood emergency:

## 1 FLOOD BOARDS & SANDBAGS

Have flood boards fitted to your home. They are a most efficient way of stopping water getting in and can be fitted by a competent DIY person.

If you know or suspect that your property is liable to flooding you should contact the district council and enquire about the availability of sandbags.

The National Rivers Authority (emergency operations) may also be able to provide additional stocks of sandbags and should be contacted on tel. 0733 371811.

## 2 WARNINGS

If there is a real threat of flooding, warnings will be given as early as possible by:

**(a)** Sirens: These are placed at strategic points along the coast. They are sounded for six intermittent periods, each of one minute duration at 15 second intervals. The whole sequence to be repeated after an interval of 15 minutes.

**(b)** Broadcasts: Announcements will be made on radio and television; in particular, BBC Radio Lincolnshire will provide full details. Tune in to 219 metres (1368 k/Hz medium wave, or 94.9M/HZ VHF).

**(c)** Loud-hailers: Police will normally tour the high risk areas in cars with loud-hailers; they will endeavour to visit as many houses as possible to make sure you have heard the warning and to offer assistance wherever possible.

**(d)** Testing: Please note that sirens are tested by the police normally in mid-August; the actual time and date will be published through the normal channels.

## 3 IF YOU HEAR A WARNING

- *Stay calm*
- *Tell your neighbours (especially if they are old or infirm)*
- *Continue to listen to BBC Radio Lincolnshire*
- *Try to move your most valuable objects to a place of safety as quickly as possible, or protect them by tying them into plastic bags*
- *Fasten your outer doors and fix your flood boards and/or sandbags*
- *Switch off gas and electricity if flooding seems imminent*
- *Move upstairs (if possible)*
- *Take food, clothes, blankets, candles or torches with you*
- *Fill bath (buckets) with water for washing, etc. (in case the mains supply has to be shut off); drinking water should be stored in clean bottles or other suitable containers*
- *Remember the pets (and a dirt tray or newspapers)*
- *Take the radio (preferably a battery portable) and continue to listen in.*

## 4 BUNGALOWS & BASEMENTS

If you live in either, try to make arrangements in advance to shelter with neighbours who have upstairs accommodation.

If you cannot find alternative accommodation, be ready to move to an evacuation centre if serious flooding threatens your area (see para. 7). Leave a message (to say where you have gone) with neighbours, or pin a note to your door.

## 5 ELDERLY OR INFIRM?

If you think you may need special help (e.g. if you are blind, deaf or disabled) try to make arrangements in advance with neighbours.

If this is not possible, make sure that you tell the police who call at your home that you need assistance.

If you live next door to somebody who may fall into this category, please be a "good neighbour" and offer to help them make arrangements.

## 6 EMERGENCY REST/FEEDING CENTRES

These are normally used under evacuation procedures, by the emergency services, and are in designated schools, village halls and community centres. They will normally be manned by the volunteer services and transport to the centres will be organised by the emergency services.

## 7 IF YOU ARE FLOODED

- *Switch off gas and electricity.*
- *If you have not already left home, you may want some or all of your family to be evacuated. Stay where you are and wait for the emergency services to come to you.*
- *It is particularly important that you do not use any contaminated foodstuffs. Utensils that have been in flood water should be cleaned and boiled thoroughly before use.*
- *You can help by not calling the police or emergency services unless it is absolutely vital.*
- *If you want further information, continue to listen to BBC Radio Lincolnshire.*

# THE PROJECT

What do you think would happen, if we took the Noah story and placed it in a present day situation of a flood alert? The ancient story set within a flood emergency today could create some interesting and humorous dramatic tensions which could form the basis of an independent performance project.

Imagine that Noah and his family live in a suburban home in an area threatened by flood. What then would happen if Noah received forewarning of a massive flood that would engulf everything? Look again at the guidance notes above and then ask yourselves what sort of situations might arise. Some of these may involve just Noah and his family, other situations will focus on people in the community, some scenes may include both.

Developing the idea may be easier if:

● you think of Noah and his family as normal human beings rather than as great mythical figures from the Bible. So the scenes should be naturalistic in style using everyday rather than 'biblical' language.

● the scenes follow what happens *after* Noah receives the call to build the ark and avoid the issue of *why* the flood is coming.

Here are some suggestions for scenes to get you started:

**Before the flood warning**

1 Neighbours seeing Noah building his ark in the garden speculate about what he is up to.

2 A policeman arrives at Noah's house to investigate a complaint that a 'great boat thing' is causing an obstruction.

3 Family discussion in Noah's house about how they are going to find a male and female of every animal. Two of the sons, Shem and Ham, are not sure they want any part in the enterprise.

4 A reporter with the local newspaper seeks an interview with Noah and his family.

**After the warning**

5 The local Civil Emergency Committee meets to work out what sort of advice they should give to the population in their area.

6 Another family – they discuss what to do about the old man who lives next door to their bungalow and who happens to have spare accommodation in a third floor attic.

7 Noah and Mrs Noah cause congestion at the local supermarket. They need food, clothes, candles, torches, etc. for at least 100 days.

8 At the police station. Noah still has not found all the animals he needs. Could the police perhaps help with their loud-hailers?

9 Another household – the family pet has gone missing and suspicion falls on Noah.

The project could involve a large group of performers sub-divided into groups. For the performance you will require only a few objects such as blankets and torches. The building of the ark could be done through noises of hammering and sawing offstage.

# OTHER FLOOD STORIES

This flood story comes from Siberia in Russia. It has some interesting variations on the Bible story – Noah's wife is a more central character, and perhaps to your surprise, the Devil appears.

## Noj and the Flood

Noj was a good man at a time when every other man was bad; or so God thought. At any rate he had decided to drown the lot of them, all except Noj, whom he warned in a whisper, 'Build a boat, Noj, build a boat.' And since Noj was accustomed to obeying the word of God, so he did, going deep into the forest each day and building it secretly from the best timbers. The only other person who knew about it was his wife.

The Devil grew very curious. He sidled up to Noj's wife one morning and said, 'Do me a favour, lady, tell me just what that man of yours is up to.'

'Certainly not,' said Noj's wife virtuously. 'It's between him and me and God, and has nothing whatever to do with you.'

'Suppose,' said the Devil, 'I were to offer you . . .'

'And whatever can you offer me, you ugly little runt?'

'A sweet tongue,' said the Devil, 'for a start; or beauty, or anything you like, a lighter hand with the baking, a speedier hand on the spindle; if only you tell me what Noj is making in the forest.'

'If I did,' said Noj's wife, 'I can't see you providing them.'

'Well then, wouldn't you like to know why Noj is doing whatever he is doing in the forest? Did he tell you that? Don't say you haven't been a little anxious.'

'I did wonder, that is the truth,' said Noj's wife, 'I hope he's not crazy, but . . .'

'So what harm can there be in it?'

Noj's wife sighed. 'Would you promise to tell me anything you find out?'

'Cross my heart, lady, and hope to die,' the Devil said.

So Noj's wife told the Devil that Noj was building a boat. And the Devil looked wise and went away and when he came back a few hours later told her that God was planning to send them on a long sea voyage, but he couldn't tell her why because even Noj didn't know that yet.

'But how's he going to get the boat from the forest to the river?' asked Noj's wife in astonishment.

'Perhaps he could do with some advice from me,' said the Devil and went away again. But from that time on, while Noj continued to build his boat by day, at night, secretly, the Devil crept in and undid his work, pulling out nails and breaking up timbers; thus each morning Noj had to begin work all over again.

'There's a jinx on me,' said Noj, crossly. 'At this rate I'll never get it done before the flood comes.' He worked harder and harder but all to no avail, and every day the skies grew heavier. Noj prayed to God then, but God was too busy preparing for the flood to take any notice of the Devil's activities (indeed he did not think he needed to, now that he planned to wipe out all the Devil's disciples). Nor did he hear Noj's prayer; until one day, at last, great drops of rain began to fall. Noj laid down his hammer and his saw and got down on his knees and prayed to God harder than ever.

'It's much too soon, God, my boat is not nearly finished, through no fault of mine. In fact I was beginning to think you didn't want me to finish it. Yet you promised to save us. Oh help me, God.' At that moment Noj's wife appeared with all her children clinging to her skirts and all her chickens and cows and pigs and sheep behind.

'I thought your boat could save us, husband, but whatever kind of boat is it?' she said. For the boat had only ribs and framework still, it had no planking, let alone a cabin with a roof, made of stout timbers caulked with pitch as Noj had planned it. 'Oh woe, oh woe, we'll all be drowned,' cried she.

From beyond the forest her cries were echoed as the waters rose; men climbed to the tops of their houses and clung to them helplessly, lashed by rain and wind. They took their animals with them if they could, all the rest were left floating on the tide. Noj and his family dragged themselves and their animals up the framework of his boat until they reached the highest point. But the waters went on rising all the time. And now dead people came floating past besides dead animals.

'Oh God,' prayed Noj, 'I am a virtuous man and why did you tell me to build my boat if you did not want me saved?'

'Oh God,' prayed Noj's wife, 'why did you ever let me have anything to do with the Devil?'

The water was already about their feet. But now something else moved gently towards them – 'Like a *boat*,' cried one of the children. 'It *is* a boat,' another said. It struck the timbers of Noj's unfinished boat with a dull clang and waited while they all scrambled down to it. But they did not find wood beneath their feet this time. When they bent down and touched the deck, their hands met something cool and smooth and hard, that glimmered faintly in the dying light, that was the same colour as the rain itself. 'This boat is made of iron,' said Noj. 'God has sent it to us surely. There never was such a miracle.'

'Better than a lighter hand with the baking or speedier hand with the spindle any day,' said his wife. But Noj did not know what she was talking about.

So it was that Noj and his wife and their children, their chickens and cows and pigs and sheep were saved from the flood that engulfed all the rest of mankind. They floated away on their iron boat while the thunder boomed and the lightning flashed and the rain fell unceasingly. In the end there was no land to be seen at all.

And if when the flood subsided they were the only people left upon earth, nonetheless there they were and it wasn't wholly the Devil's to do what he liked with. One thing was certain, Noj's wife would never listen to that voice again: though one can't say the same of all her descendants.

*Penelope Farmer*

83

The story provides a useful structure for building a play of your own on the theme of the flood. It has plenty of good situations for drama – Noah being stressed by trying to complete the boat on time, his frustration that his work is constantly undone, his appeals to God, the curiosity of the Devil and the temptation of Mrs Noah, her guilty secret and the miracle of the iron boat. As well as taking scenes directly from the play, you could add some of your own; for example, the Devil at night organises a group of other devils to sabotage Noah's work and Noah accuses his neighbours of doing the damage.

Another way of using the story is to tell the story (without script) to a small audience. You could do this individually, in pairs or in threes. This is a very good exercise to do as part of your work in drama. It makes you focus on what is dramatic about the story and on simple techniques for bringing character and situation alive in the telling.

However you chose to tell the story, do not attempt to learn the words, or even write your own words down, they will only sound false. Telling the story directly will be the best. This may mean losing some of the printed story, but with practice you will learn to add some bits of your own, and that is when the story comes alive. But there are things you can do to help prepare yourself for telling the story:

---

**1**

Divide the story into sections. (One paragraph in the printed story could give you more than one section.)

e.g.
**(a)**
God thinks over his plan for the world.

**(b)**
God gives instructions to Noah to build a boat.

**(c)**
Noah starts to build the boat in secret in the forest.

**(d)**
The Devil arrives and shows interest in the boat and persuades Mrs Noah to give him information.
etc.

---

**2**

In your imagination create a picture for each section. Give yourself time to imagine it – Who's in the picture? What do they look like? What's happening? Does the picture have colours, sounds? (Work in pairs here – A creates the picture and B asks questions about what A can see.)

**3**

Out of all the pictures choose one which feels like the key turning point in the story, i.e. the picture that the other pictures are working towards.

↓

**4**

Run the pictures in your mind in sequence rather like a film or slides in a projector. Know how each picture follows on from the one before and how the sequence builds to the special picture at the heart of the story.

↓

**5**

Now try telling the story, picture by picture, to a partner or a small group.

If you can enter into your pictures and describe what you see, your listeners will enter with you. Concentrate on the pictures and the words will follow.

If you tell the story in twos or threes, the same principles apply. Working with others gives you more scope to act out the story *as you tell it*, and to use movements and objects in symbolic ways (as suggested in earlier sections of these notes); for example:

- For the flood you could use a strip of blue cloth stretched on the floor, raising it slowly to represent the rising water level.

- Characterisation – the Devil need not be the horned animal we see in pictures, but could instead be a smooth-talking gentleman in a pin-stripe suit.

- Group images – a family clinging together on a chimney top as the waters rise. Their eyes together follow things that float past them.

Here is another story for similar treatment. It comes from Indians on the North-West Pacific coast of America.

## Mount Rainier and the Great Flood

Long, long ago, when the earth was young, the Great Spirit became very angry with the people and the animals of his world. The Great Spirit lived on the snowy summit of Takhoma.

He was angry because the people and animals were wicked and did many mean things to each other. He decided that he would rid the earth of all of them except the good animals and one good man and his family.

So he said to the good man, 'Shoot an arrow into that cloud hanging low over the mountain.'

The good man shot an arrow, and it stuck in the cloud.

'Now shoot another arrow into the shaft of that arrow,' continued the Great Spirit.

The second arrow hit the lower part of the first arrow and stuck there. The man kept on shooting arrows, as the Great Spirit commanded, and each arrow stuck in the lower part of the preceding arrow. After a while there was a long rope of arrows reaching from the cloud on top of the mountain clear down to the ground.

'Now tell your wife and children,' commanded the Great Spirit, 'to climb up that rope of arrows. Tell the good animals to climb up after them. But don't let the bad people and bad animals go up.'

So the good man sent his wife up the arrow rope, then his children, and then the good animals. He watched them climb into the cloud above the mountain. Then the good man himself climbed up.

Just as he was stepping into the cloud, he looked back. Coming up the arrow rope was a long line of bad animals and snakes. They were climbing towards the cloud. So the good man took hold of the arrows nearest him and broke the rope. He watched all the bad animals and the snakes tumble down the sides of the mountain.

When the Great Spirit saw that the good animals and the good people were safe around him, he caused a heavy rain to fall. It rained and rained and rained and rained for many days and many nights. All the earth was under water. The water rose higher and higher on the sides of Takhoma. At last it came up to the snow line, up to the high place where the snow leaves off in the summertime.

By that time all the bad people and all the bad animals were drowned. So the Great Spirit commanded the rain to stop. He and the good man and his family watched the waters slowly go down. The land became dry again.

Then the Great Spirit said to the good man, 'Now you may take your family and the animals back to the earth.'

So they all climbed out of the cloud, and the good man led them down a mountain-trail to the place where they were to build a new lodge. As they walked down, they found no bad animals or snakes, and there have been none on Takhoma to this day.

*Ella Clark*

# 'THE FLOOD' IN MEDIEVAL 'MYSTERY' PLAYS

During the Middle Ages it was common for large cities to perform plays based on Bible stories. These plays would involve many actors and were performed in the open air on wagons, called pageants, that were pulled through the streets of the city, pausing to perform at various set points.

As few people in these times could read, the plays were as much educational as entertaining, being one of the chief ways in which people would learn of events in the Old and New Testament.

Each episode was performed by a different group of actors. These actors were not professionals, but earned their living at other trades. In any case the plays were only performed at annual festivals such as the Feast of Corpus Christi and then not every year.

People who were involved in particular trades in these times would group together for business reasons into *guilds*. Each guild was responsible for a particular biblical episode and rivalry was strong between the guilds as to who could do the best and most lavish performance. There was often a link between the trades and the play which they performed. The story of Abraham and Isaac, which deals with animal and human sacrifice, was often performed by the Butchers' Guild. Joseph, with his coat of many colours, was often performed by the Weavers' Guild, and so on.

Noah and the Flood was often performed by the Carpenters' Guild and may well have been one of the most difficult to stage. Not only would an ark need to be built, but also the animals would have to be represented in some way or other.

Although few people could read, the plays were often scripted. Some of these scripts still survive and a number have been translated and revised quite recently.

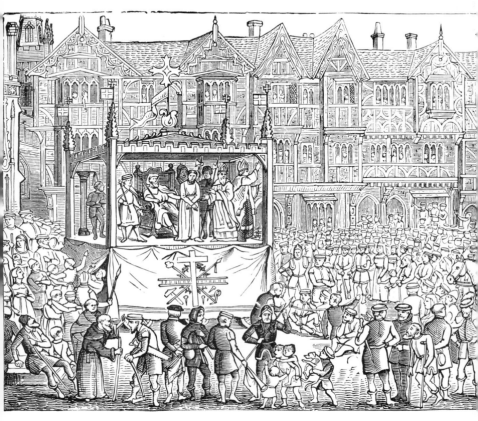

A representation of what the performance of these biblical or mystery plays might have looked like.

Here is an extract from a modern translation by Tony Harrison of the
York, Chester, Wakefield and Coventry mystery plays, performed by
the National Theatre. All four plays have been combined into one, with
some modern songs included. The writer has attempted to keep the
original sound of the speech whilst making it rather easier for a modern
audience to understand. Noah, in this extract, is trying to persuade his
wife to join him in the Ark.


**WIFE**               Here shall no man tarry thee; I pray thee to go!
                       Full well may we miss thee, as ever have I rue. To
                       spin will I set me.

*She sits down to spin.*

**NOAH**               Whey! farewell, lo!
                       But wife,
                       Pray for me busily,
                       Till after I come to thee.
**WIFE**               Even as thou pray'st for me,
                       As ever might I thrive.
**NOAH**               I tarry full long from my work, I trow;
                       Now my gear will I bring and thitherward draw.

*He goes to build his ship. The keel is brought on.*

                       Now assay will I
                       What I know of shipwrightry
                       *In nomine Patris, et Fillii,*
                       *Et Spiritus Sancti. Amen.*
                       To begin with this tree my bones will I bend.
                       I trust that the Trinity succour will send.

*Shipwrights enter. The Ark is built. Noah speaks from the Ark.*

                       Wife, have done; come into ship fast.
**WIFE**               (*spinning*) Aye, Noah, go clout thy shoon! The
                       better will they last.

| | |
|---|---|
| **NOAH** | Now is this twice come in, dame, on my friendship. |
| **WIFE** | Whether I lose or I win, in faith, thy fellowship, Set I not at a pin. This spindle will I slip Up this hill Ere I stir once a foot. |
| **NOAH** | Peter! I trow that we dote. Without any more note, Come in if ye will. |
| **WIFE** | Aye, the water nighs so near that I sit not dry; Into ship with a fleer, therefore, will I hie For dread that I drown here. |

*She hurries to the Ark. Then she turns to women in the audience.*

Lord, I were at ease, and in heart quite whole,
Might I once have a mess of widow's cawl.
For *thy* soul, without lies, should I deal penny dole:
So would more, and no fuss, that I see in this hall
Among wives that are here,
For the life that they lead
Wish their husbands were dead;
For, as ever eat I bread,
So wish I our sire were!

**Noah** *turns to the men in the audience.*

**NOAH**    Ye men that have wives, whiles they are young,
If ye love your own lives, chastise their tongue.
Methink my heart rives – and both liver and lung –
To see such-like strifes wedded men among.

**NOAH** *goes to steer the Ark.*

Now to the helm will I hent,
And to my ship attend.

| | |
|---|---|
| **WIFE** | I see in the firmament, Methinks, the seven stars. |
| **NOAH** | This is a great flood, wife, take heed. |

| WIFE | So methought, as I stood. We are in great dread; These waves are so wode. |
|------|--------------------------------------------------------------------------|
| NOAH | Help, God, in this need! As thou art steersman good, and the best, as I rede, Of all, Thou rule us in this race, As thou did me promise. |
| WIFE | This is a perilous case. Help, God, when we call! |

*Song: 'When my Ship comes in'.*

| BAND | Oh the time will come up. When the winds will stop. And the seas will cease to be a breathing, Like the stillness in the wind, Before the hurricane begins, The hour that our ship comes in. Then the sands will roll out a carpet of gold. For your weary toes to be a touching And the ship's wise men will remind you once again That the whole wide world is watching. |
|------|----------------------------------------------------------------------------|

*(Words and music: Bob Dylan)*

The full play, *Noah and His Sons*, on which this scene is based, can be found in the Wakefield Mystery Plays. These are published under the title *The Complete Plays of the Wakefield Master* by Heinemann Educational Books (version by John Russell Brown).

You might try taking a Bible story yourselves in groups of six and find out if you can construct a simple script or performance out of it.

Try taking your performance outdoors to the playground or playing field. Examine what differences this makes to the way you have to speak and move.

Imagine yourself to be a member of the Carpenters' Guild in a large city during the Middle Ages. Write down the suggestions you would make for how the animals going into the Ark might be performed.